S0-AZY-219

PRIMARY MATHEMATICS

WORKBOOK 3B

Common Core Edition

SINGAPORE MATH® PROGRAM

mc Marshall Cavendish
Education

Original edition published under the title Primary Mathematics Workbook 3B
© 1981 Curriculum Planning & Development Division, Ministry of Education, Singapore
Published by Times Media Private Limited

This edition © 2014 Marshall Cavendish Education Pte Ltd

Published by Marshall Cavendish Education
Times Centre, 1 New Industrial Road, Singapore 536196
Customer Service Hotline: (65) 6213 9444
US Office Tel: (1-914) 332 8888 | Fax: (1-914) 332 8882
E-mail: tmesales@mceducation.com
Website: www.mceducation.com

First published 2014
Reprinted 2014, 2016, 2017, 2018 (twice)

All rights reserved.

No part of this publication may be reproduced, stored in a retrieval system
or transmitted, in any form or by any means, electronic, mechanical,
photocopying, recording or otherwise, without the prior permission
of the copyright owner. Any requests for permission should be
addressed to the Publisher.

Marshall Cavendish is a registered trademark of Times Publishing Limited.

Singapore Math® is a trademark of Singapore Math Inc.® and
Marshall Cavendish Education Pte Ltd.

Primary Mathematics (Common Core Edition) Workbook 3B
ISBN 978-981-01-9846-6

Printed in Singapore

Primary Mathematics (Common Core Edition) is adapted from Primary Mathematics Workbook 3B (3rd Edition), originally
developed by the Ministry of Education, Singapore. This edition contains new content developed by Marshall Cavendish
Education Pte Ltd, which is not attributable to the Ministry of Education, Singapore.

We would like to acknowledge the contributions by:

The Project Team from the Ministry of Education, Singapore that developed the original Singapore edition
Project Director: Dr Kho Tek Hong
Team Members: Hector Chee Kum Hoong, Liang Hin Hoon, Lim Eng Tann,
              Ng Siew Lee, Rosalind Lim Hui Cheng, Ng Hwee Wan

Primary Mathematics (Common Core Edition)
Richard Askey, Emeritus Professor of Mathematics from University of Wisconsin, Madison
Jennifer Kempe, Curriculum Advisor from Singapore Math Inc.®

CONTENTS

EXERCISE 1

1. Write **heavier than**, **lighter than**, or **as heavy as**.

   (a)

   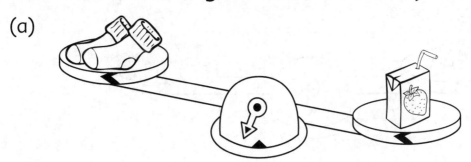

   The pair of socks is _____ the juice pack.

   (b)

   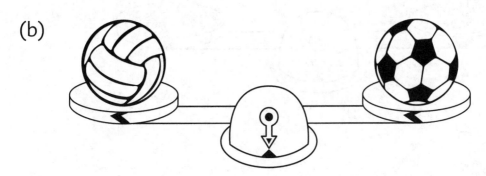

   The volleyball is _____ the soccer ball.

   (c)

   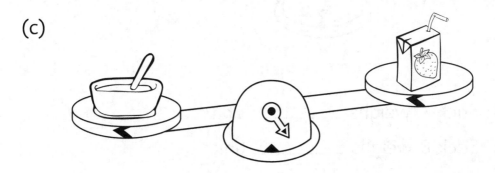

   The bowl of soup is _____ the juice pack.

   (d) The pair of socks is _____ the bowl of soup.

2. Use 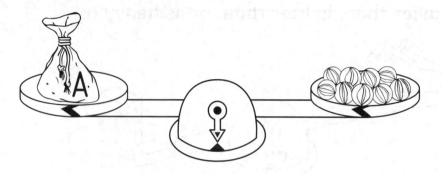 as 1 unit.

(a) Sack A weighs _____ units.

(b) Sack B weighs _____ units.

(c) Sack C weighs _____ units.

(d) Sack A is lighter than Sack _____.

(e) Arrange the sacks in increasing order of weight.

Sack _____, Sack _____, Sack _____

EXERCISE 2

1. You need a balance and a kilogram mass.

   Put a check (✓) in the correct box.

	Less than 1 kg	More than 1 kg
Mass of a pair of shoes		
Mass of 5 textbooks		

2. Work in groups. Find some items that you think have a mass of between 1 kg and 5 kg. Estimate, and then measure their masses. Record their masses as **between** _____ **kg** **and** _____ **kg**, or **exactly** _____ **kg**.

Object	My estimate	My measure

3. Fill in the blanks.

(a) The pineapple has a mass of _____ kg.

(b) The watermelon has a mass of _____ kg.

(c) The pumpkin has a mass of _____ kg.

(d) The pumpkin is _____ kg heavier than the watermelon.

(e) The total mass of the pineapple, watermelon, and pumpkin is _____ kg.

4. Samuel had a mass of 63 kg a year ago.
   His mass is 45 kg now.
   How many kilograms did Samuel lose?

5. Janet has a mass of 45 kg.
    She is 22 kg lighter than her mother.
    What is the mass of Janet's mother?

---

6. The mass of a box of books is 127 kg.
    83 kg of books are added to the box.
    Find the final mass of the box of books.

---

7. The total mass of Bob's luggage and Freda's luggage is 92 kg.
    The mass of Bob's luggage is 45 kg.
    What is the mass of Freda's luggage?

8. Jack had a mass of 17 kg ten years ago.
    He is three times as heavy now.
    How heavy is Jack now?

---

9. A café has 48 kg of coffee beans.
    The coffee beans are packed into 8 boxes.
    What is the mass of 1 box of coffee beans?

---

10. Mrs. Tyler uses 5 kg of fertilizer each week.
    How much fertilizer does she use in a year (52 weeks)?

EXERCISE 3

1. Work in groups. Find some objects that have a mass of less than 1 kg. Estimate, and then measure their masses.

Object	My estimate	My measure
	About _____ g	About _____ g
	About _____ g	About _____ g
	About _____ g	About _____ g
	About _____ g	About _____ g

2. Fill in the blanks.

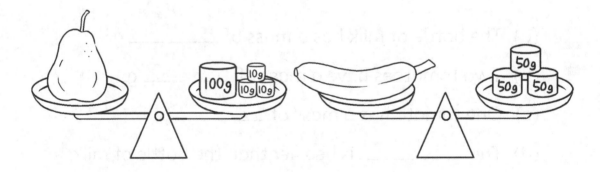

(a) The pear has a mass of ☐ g.

(b) The banana has a mass of ☐ g.

(c) The total mass of the fruits is ☐ g.

(d) The pear is ☐ g lighter than the banana.

3. Fill in the blanks with **kg** or **g**.

   (a) A loaf of bread has a mass of about 1 _____.

   (b) A dollar bill has a mass of about 1 _____.

   (c) A bag of peanuts has a mass of about 100 _____.

   (d) A horse has a mass of about 500 _____.

   (e) A baby has a mass of about 6 _____.

4. Fill in the blanks.

   (a) The bottle of milk has a mass of _____ g.

   (b) Two tomatoes have a mass of _____ g.

   (c) One tomato has a mass of _____ g.

   (d) The _____ is heavier than the bottle of milk.

   (e) The bottle of milk is _____ g heavier than the tomatoes.

5. Cheryl bought some flour to bake muffins.
   She used 785 g and had 145 g left.
   How much flour did she have at first?

_____

6. The mass of a bottle of sand is 256 g.
   The mass of the empty bottle is 180 g.
   What is the mass of the sand?

_____

7. A pear is 260 g lighter than a papaya.
   Find the mass of the pear.

8. Each tube of watercolor weighs 82 g.
    What is the total mass of 7 tubes of watercolor?

---

9. The total mass of 6 bags of licorice is 990 g.
    What is the mass of 1 bag of licorice?

---

10. Tricia sends a package that has a mass of 270 g.
    Ruth sends a package that is twice as heavy as Tricia's parcel.
    What is the mass of Ruth's package?

EXERCISE 4

1. Write the mass of each of the following.

    (a)

    _____ kg _____ g

    (b)

    _____ kg _____ g

    (c)

    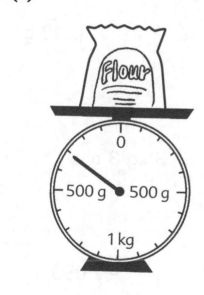

    _____ kg _____ g

    (d)

    _____ kg _____ g

EXERCISE 5

1. Draw a straight line to join each pair of equal masses.
   If you do it correctly, you will trap each animal in a shape.

1 kg 100 g   1 kg 250 g

                                • 1 kg 25 g

1 kg 10 g

                    • 1,100 g

1,250 g

                                2 kg 25 g

2 kg 50 g

                                1,010 g

1,025 g

3 kg 80 g   3 kg 8 g

2,025 g   • 2,050 g

            • 3,080 g

3,008 g

2. Write the following in grams.

    (a) 1 kg 800 g = _____ g

    (b) 6 kg   20 g = _____ g

    (c) 2 kg 300 g = _____ g

    (d) 9 kg   2 g = _____ g

    (e) 4 kg   83 g = _____ g

    (f) 8 kg   15 g = _____ g

3. Write the following in kilograms and grams.

    (a) 1,280 g = _____ kg _____ g

    (b) 4,069 g = _____ kg _____ g

    (c) 2,506 g = _____ kg _____ g

    (d) 5,108 g = _____ kg _____ g

    (e) 3,009 g = _____ kg _____ g

    (f) 6,004 g = _____ kg _____ g

4. Fill in each ( ) with >, <, or =.

    (a) 3 kg 5 g ( ) 3,050 g   (b) 2 kg 20 g ( ) 2,020 g

    (c) 4 kg 8 g ( ) 4,010 g   (d) 1 kg 86 g ( ) 1,086 g

5. (a) Which is heavier, the duck or the hen?

1 kg 50 g   1,550 g

The _____ is heavier than the _____.

(b) Which is lighter?

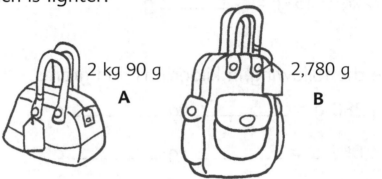

2 kg 90 g   2,780 g
A   B

Bag _____ is lighter than Bag _____.

6. Fill in the blanks.

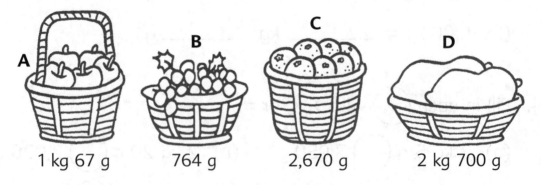

1 kg 67 g   764 g   2,670 g   2 kg 700 g

(a) Basket _____ is the heaviest.

(b) Basket _____ is the lightest.

(c) Basket A is heavier than Basket _____.

(d) Basket C is lighter than Basket _____.

EXERCISE 6

1. Write the missing numbers.

(a)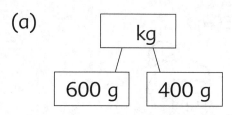

(b)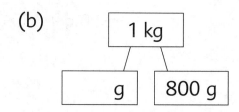

(c)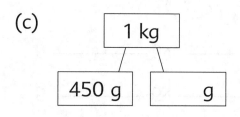

(d)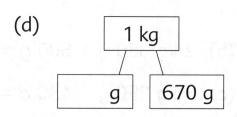

(e) 1 kg − 750 g = _____ g

(f) 1 kg − 390 g = _____ g

(g) 1 kg − 150 g = _____ g

(h) 1 kg − 220 g = _____ g

(i) 3 kg − 250 g = _____ kg _____ g

(j) 10 kg − 830 g = _____ kg _____ g

2. Add.

   (a) 1 kg 300 g + 550 g = _____ kg _____ g

   300 g + 550 g = 850 g

   (b) 2 kg 650 g + 600 g = _____ kg _____ g

   (c) 3 kg 850 g + 430 g = _____ kg _____ g

3. Add in compound units.

   (a) 2 kg 245 g + 1 kg 520 g = _____ kg _____ g

   2 kg 245 g $\xrightarrow{+\,1\,kg}$ 3 kg 245 g $\xrightarrow{+\,520\,g}$ 3 kg 765 g

   (b) 4 kg 680 g + 1 kg 570 g = _____ kg _____ g

   (c) 3 kg 95 g + 2 kg 960 g = _____ kg _____ g

   (d) 4 kg 804 g + 3 kg 205 g = _____ kg _____ g

4. Subtract.

(a) 4 kg 850 g − 760 g = _____ kg _____ g

850 g − 760 g = 90 g

(b) 5 kg 25 g − 480 g = _____ kg _____ g

(c) 7 kg 200 g − 365 g = _____ kg _____ g

5. Subtract in compound units.

(a) 2 kg 924 g − 1 kg 768 g = _____ kg _____ g

2 kg 924 g $\xrightarrow{-\,1\,kg}$ 1 kg 924 g $\xrightarrow{-\,768\,g}$ 1 kg 156 g

(b) 4 kg 30 g − 1 kg 288 g = _____ kg _____ g

(c) 3 kg 145 g − 2 kg 295 g = _____ kg _____ g

(d) 10 kg 5 g − 3 kg 269 g = _____ kg _____ g

EXERCISE 7

Find the mass of the following.

1. (a) Total mass of the
        toothpaste and the book
        =

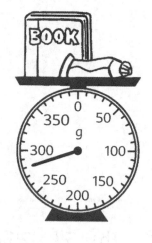

    (b) The mass of the
        toothpaste is 100 g.

        Mass of the book
        =

2. (a) Mass of the jar of sand
        =

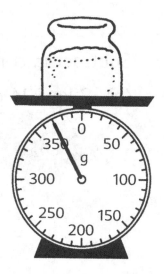

    (b) The mass of the
        empty jar is 150 g.

        Mass of the sand
        =

3. (a) Total mass of the fruit
        =

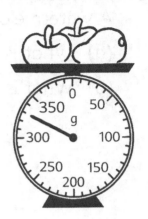

    (b) The pear has a mass of 130 g.

        Mass of the 2 apples
        =

    (c) Both apples have the same mass.

        Mass of each apple
        =

4. (a) Total mass of 2 tennis balls
        and 5 marbles
        =

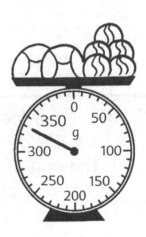

    (b) Each tennis ball has a mass of 60 g.

        Mass of 2 tennis balls
        =

        Mass of 5 marbles
        =

    (c) The marbles have the same mass.

        Mass of each marble
        =

5. A pineapple has a mass of 2 kg 50 g.
   A watermelon is 600 g heavier than the pineapple.

   (a) What is the mass of the watermelon?

   (b) What is the total mass of the two fruits?

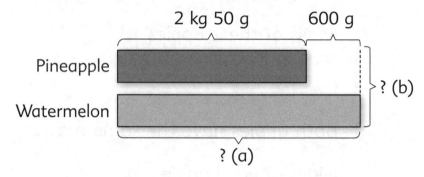

6. The total mass of a bag of flour and a bag of salt is
   2 kg 400 g.
   If the bag of flour has a mass of 1 kg 950 g, find the mass
   of the bag of salt.

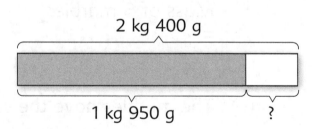

EXERCISE 8

1. Fill in the blanks with **oz** or **lb**.

    (a) 10 quarter dollars weigh about 2 _____.

    (b) A bicycle weighs about 50 _____.

    (c) A sandwich weighs about 9 _____.

    (d) A butterfly weighs about 1 _____.

    (e) A cat weighs about 5 _____.

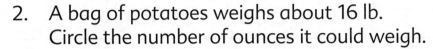

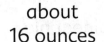

2. A bag of potatoes weighs about 16 lb.
   Circle the number of ounces it could weigh.

| about 16 ounces | about 1 ounce | about 250 ounces |

3. How many of each weight do you need to balance the weight of the book?

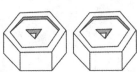
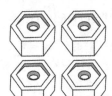

8 oz   4 oz   1 oz

23 oz

_____   _____   _____
8 oz   4 oz   1 oz
weight(s)   weight(s)   weight(s)

4. Ryan weighs 88 lb.
   Frank is 19 lb lighter than Ryan.

   (a) How much does Frank weigh?

   Frank weighs _____ lb.

   (b) Find their total weight.

   Together, they weigh _____ lb.

5. A pineapple weighs 96 oz.
   A watermelon weighs 22 oz more than the pineapple.

   (a) What is the weight of the watermelon?

   The watermelon weighs _____ oz.

   (b) What is the total weight of the pineapple and
       the watermelon?

   The total weight is _____ oz.

EXERCISE 9

1. Write the weight of each of the following.

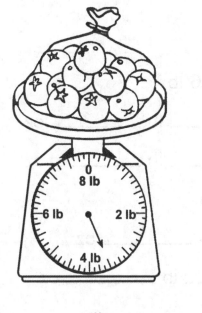 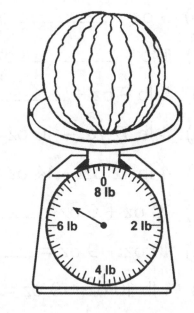

_____ lb _____ oz   _____ lb _____ oz

2. Write in ounces.

   (a) 2 lb   (b) 3 lb 10 oz   (c) 8 lb 9 oz

   _____   _____   _____

3. Write in pounds and ounces.

   (a) 18 oz   (b) 22 oz   (c) 32 oz

   _____   _____   _____

4. Fill in each ◯ with >, <, or =.

   (a) 1 lb 6 oz ◯ 21 oz   (b) 9 lb 11 oz ◯ 157 oz

   (c) 16 oz ◯ 1 lb   (d) 20 oz ◯ 1 lb 2 oz

5. Find the missing numbers.

   (a) 8 oz + 8 oz = _____ oz

   (b) 3 oz + _____ oz = 1 lb

   (c) 1 lb − _____ oz = 10 oz

   (d) 5 lb 9 oz + _____ oz = 6 lb

   (e) 4 lb 12 oz − 10 oz = _____ lb _____ oz

   (f) 4 lb 12 oz − 14 oz = _____ lb _____ oz

   (g) 10 oz + 6 oz = _____ lb

   (h) 10 oz + 9 oz = _____ lb _____ oz

   (i) 1 lb 10 oz + 9 oz = _____ lb _____ oz

   (j) 4 oz + 14 oz = _____ lb _____ oz

   (k) 1 lb 13 oz + 10 oz = _____ lb _____ oz

   (l) 4 lb 9 oz + _____ oz = 5 lb 1 oz

6. A pumpkin weighs 8 lb.
   An apple weighs 4 oz.
   What is the difference in their weight?

EXERCISE 10

1. Add in compound units.

    (a) 5 lb 5 oz + 7 lb 12 oz = _____ lb _____ oz

    $$5 \text{ lb } 5 \text{ oz } \xrightarrow{+ \, 7 \text{ lb}} 12 \text{ lb } 5 \text{ oz } \xrightarrow{+ \, 12 \text{ oz}} 13 \text{ lb } 1 \text{ oz}$$

    (b) 3 lb 4 oz + 8 lb 12 oz = _____ lb _____ oz

    (c) 2 lb 9 oz + 4 lb 8 oz = _____ lb _____ oz

2. Subtract in compound units.

    (a) 5 lb 5 oz − 2 lb 15 oz = _____ lb _____ oz

    (b) 12 lb − 10 lb 2 oz = _____ lb _____ oz

    (c) 8 lb 11 oz − 7 lb 12 oz = _____ lb _____ oz

3. Solve the following.

    (a) Weight of the asparagus =

    (b) Ms. Wright paid $9 for the asparagus.
         Cost of 1 lb of asparagus =

    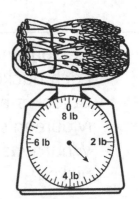

4. Mr. Green buys 2 pumpkins.
    1 pumpkin weighs 7 lb 10 oz.
    The other pumpkin weighs 9 lb 7 oz.
    What is the total weight of the 2 pumpkins?

5. The total weight of 2 watermelons is 20 lb 7 oz.
One watermelon weighs 13 lb 9 oz.
What is the weight of the smaller watermelon?

---

6. 2 packages of cheese and a box of crackers together
weigh 3 lb.
The box of crackers alone weighs 1 lb 12 oz.
How much does one package of cheese weigh?

---

7. Carson and Maureen each picked a bucket of berries.
Each bucket weighed 10 oz.
Carson's bucket of berries weighed 3 lb 14 oz.
Maureen's bucket of berries weighed 4 lb 8 oz.
What was the total weight of the berries both of them
picked?

REVIEW 6

1. Fill in the blanks with **kg** or **g**.

   (a) A watermelon has a mass of about 2 _____.

   (b) A pear has a mass of about 120 _____.

   (c) Mr. Banks buys a jar of honey that has a mass of 850 _____.

   (d) Mark bought a 5- _____ bag of rice.

2. Match.

   The weight of an apple is about •   • | 1 oz

   The weight of a man is about •   • | 15 lb

   The weight of a watermelon is about •   • | 6 oz

   The weight of a marble is about •   • | 180 lb

3. Fill in each ◯ with **>**, **<**, or **=**.

   (a) 1 kg ◯ 1 lb   (b) 4 lb ◯ 4 oz

   (c) 20 oz ◯ 1 lb 5 oz   (d) 3 lb 6 oz ◯ 36 oz

4. How heavy is each?

   (a) The mango has a mass of _____ g.

   (b) The apple has a mass of _____ g.

5. Fill in the blanks.

(a) The pumpkin has a mass of _____ kg.

(b) 1 kg of pumpkin costs $3.

   The pumpkin costs $ _____.

6. Fill in the blanks.

(a) 2 kg 65 g = _____ g

(b) 3,180 g = _____ kg _____ g

(c) 5 kg 7 g = _____ g

(d) 7,245 g = _____ kg _____ g

(e) 4 lb 3 oz = _____ oz

(f) 24 oz = _____ lb _____ oz

(g) 2 lb 12 oz = _____ oz

(h) 35 oz = _____ lb _____ oz

7. Add or subtract.

(a) 3 kg 95 g + 2 kg 75 g = _____ kg _____ g

(b) 2 kg − 650 g = _____ kg _____ g

(c) 4 kg 820 g + 3 kg 720 g = _____ kg _____ g

(d) 5 kg 60 g − 2 kg 830 g = _____ kg _____ g

(e) 16 lb 2 oz + 5 lb 11 oz = _____ lb _____ oz

(f) 7 lb 10 oz − 4 lb 5 oz = _____ lb _____ oz

(g) 18 lb 9 oz + 7 lb 9 oz = _____ lb _____ oz

(h) 15 lb 4 oz − 6 lb 13 oz = _____ lb _____ oz

8. A box of peaches has a mass of 39 kg.
A crate of watermelons is 3 times as heavy as the box of peaches.
How much heavier is the crate of watermelons than the box of peaches?

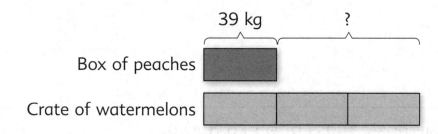

9. A bucket filled with sand has a mass of 5 kg.
    The empty bucket has a mass of 200 g.
    Find the mass of the sand in kilograms
    and grams.

---

10. Mr. Meyer had two bunches of grapes.
    One bunch weighed 2 lb 8 oz.
    The other bunch weighed 2 lb 9 oz.
    Find the total weight of the two bunches of grapes.

---

11. 9 fish and some shrimp have a mass of 6 kg.
    Each fish has a mass of 628 g.
    Find the mass of the shrimp.

---

12. Jessie has a mass of 65 kg 850 g.
    Malcolm is 12 kg 475 g heavier than Jessie.
    What is their total mass?

EXERCISE 1

1. Which container can hold more water?
   Circle it.

(a)

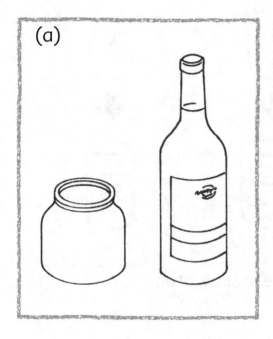

(b)

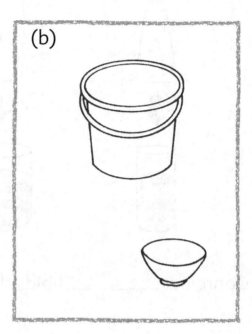

2. Which container can hold the least water?
   Circle it.

(a)

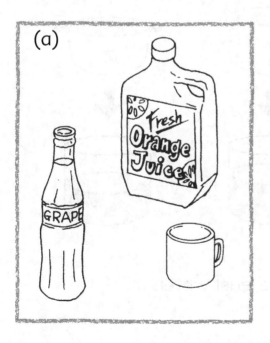

(b)

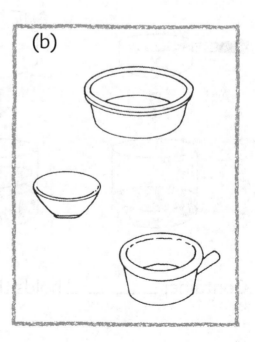

3. Which container holds the most water?

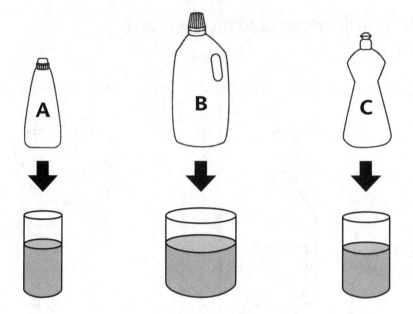

Container _____ holds the most water.

4. Which container holds the least water?

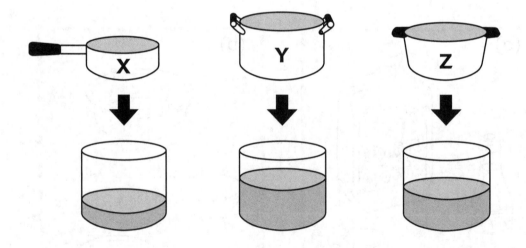

Container _____ holds the least water.

5. Fill in the blanks.

(a)

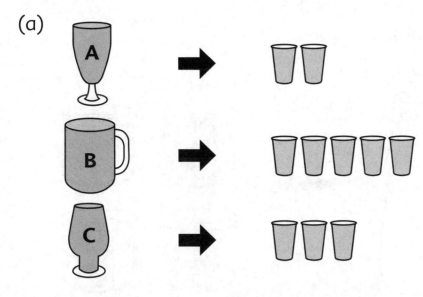

Glass _____ holds the most water.

Glass _____ holds the least water.

(b)

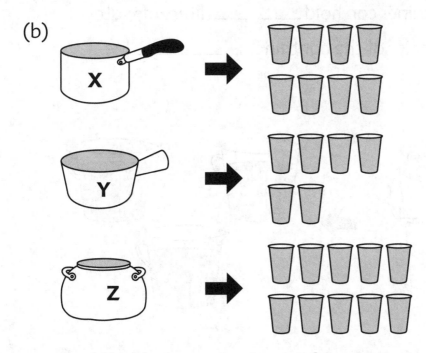

Pot X holds _____ cups of water more than Pot Y.

Pot X holds _____ cups of water less than Pot Z.

EXERCISE 2

1. Fill in the blanks.

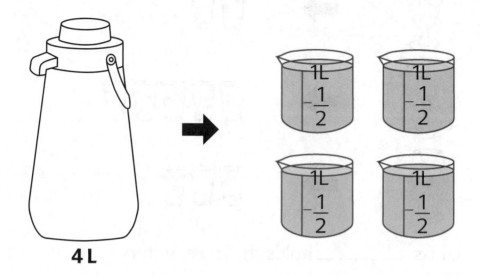

4 L

(a) The container can hold _____ liters of water.

(b) The capacity of the container is _____ liters.

2.

(a) The bucket can hold _____ liters of water.

(b) The capacity of the bucket is _____ liters.

EXERCISE 3

Work with your friends.
You need a 100-ml beaker.

1. Get a plastic bottle that can hold 1 L.

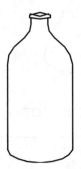

Use the bottle to make your own measuring container.

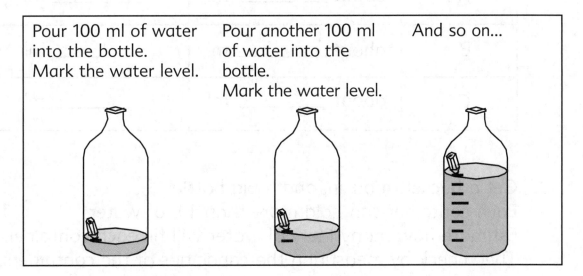

Pour 100 ml of water into the bottle. Mark the water level.

Pour another 100 ml of water into the bottle. Mark the water level.

And so on...

Your measuring container will look like this:

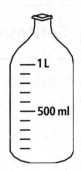

Use the measuring container you have made for the activities on the next page.

2. Get any three small containers.
   Each container has a capacity of less than 1 L.
   Label them A, B, and C as shown.

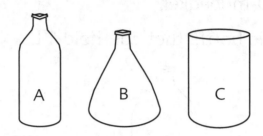

Estimate and then measure the capacity of each container.

Container	My estimate	My measure
A	about _____ ml	_____ ml
B	about _____ ml	_____ ml
C	about _____ ml	_____ ml

3. Get a bucket, a basin, and a big bottle.
   Each container can hold more than 1 L of water.
   Estimate how many liters of water will fill each container.
   Then check by measuring the capacities of the containers.

Container	My estimate	My measure
a bucket	about _____ L	___ L ___ ml
a basin	about _____ L	___ L ___ ml
a big bottle	about _____ L	___ L ___ ml

4. Match.

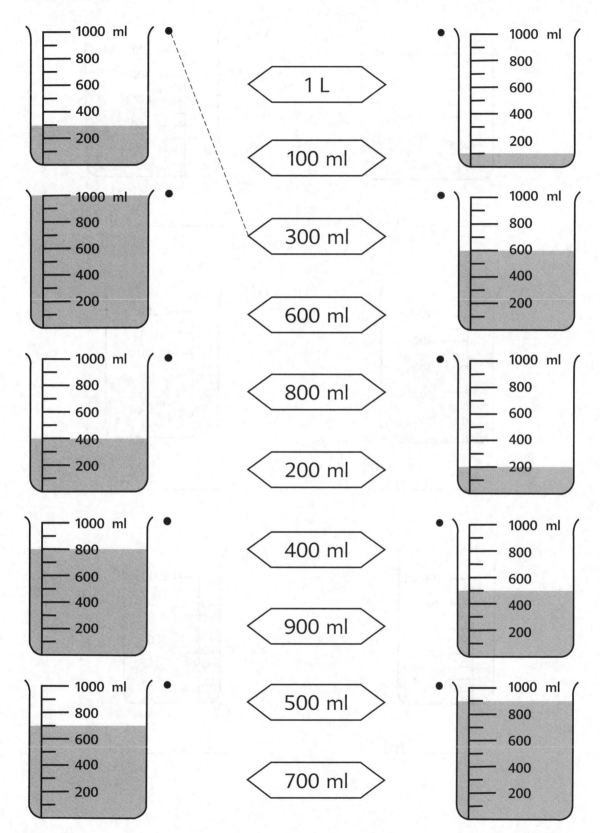

5. How much water is there in each container?

(a)

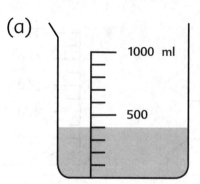

1000 ml

500

_____ ml

(b)

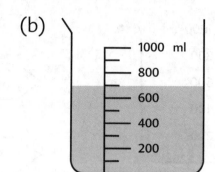

1000 ml

800

600

400

200

_____ ml

(c)

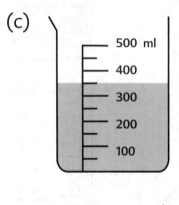

500 ml

400

300

200

100

_____ ml

(d)

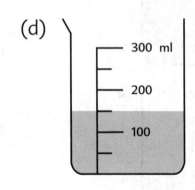

300 ml

200

100

_____ ml

(e)

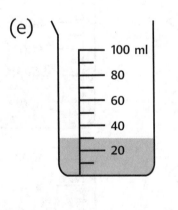

100 ml

80

60

40

20

_____ ml

(f)

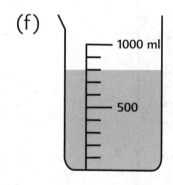

1000 ml

500

_____ ml

EXERCISE 4

1. Match.

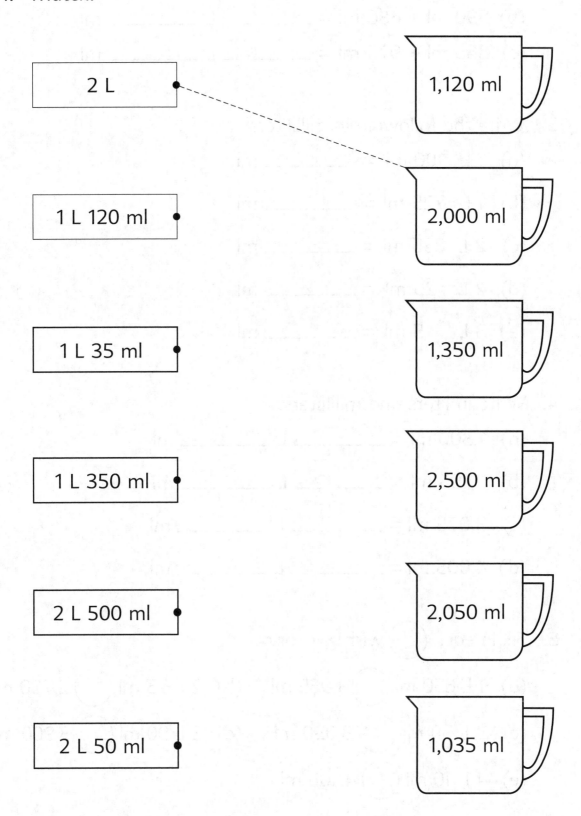

2 L	1,120 ml
1 L 120 ml	2,000 ml
1 L 35 ml	1,350 ml
1 L 350 ml	2,500 ml
2 L 500 ml	2,050 ml
2 L 50 ml	1,035 ml

2. Add.

    (a) 405 ml + 920 ml = _____ L _____ ml

    (b) 590 ml + 680 ml = _____ L _____ ml

    (c) 865 ml + 975 ml = _____ L _____ ml

3. Write the following in milliliters.

    (a) 1 L 100 ml = _____ ml

    (b) 1 L 725 ml = _____ ml

    (c) 2 L 855 ml = _____ ml

    (d) 2 L   25 ml = _____ ml

    (e) 3 L   5 ml = _____ ml

4. Write in liters and milliliters.

    (a) 1,300 ml = _____ L _____ ml

    (b) 2,105 ml = _____ L _____ ml

    (c) 3,075 ml = _____ L _____ ml

    (d) 4,005 ml = _____ L _____ ml

5. Fill in each ( ) with >, <, or =.

    (a) 1 L 650 ml ( ) 1,065 ml   (b) 2 L 75 ml ( ) 2,750 ml

    (c) 3 L 30 ml ( ) 3,030 ml   (d) 3 L 90 ml ( ) 3,900 ml

    (e) 4 L 10 ml ( ) 4,100 ml

EXERCISE 5

1. Draw a straight line to join each pair of amounts that add up to 1 L.
    If you do it correctly, you will separate the rabbits from one another.

2. Write the missing numbers.

(a)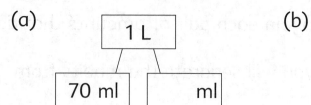

(b)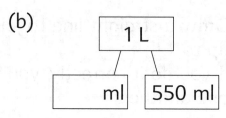

(c)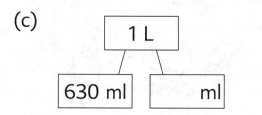

(d)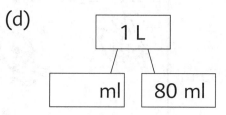

3. Write the missing numbers.

(a) 1 L − 860 ml = _____ ml

(b) 1 L − 420 ml = _____ ml

(c) 1 L − 750 ml = _____ ml

(d) 1 L − 340 ml = _____ ml

(e) 6 L − 5 L 125 ml = _____ ml

(f) 4 L − 3 L 35 ml = _____ ml

(g) 2 L − 130 ml = _____ L _____ ml

(h) 4 L − 65 ml = _____ L _____ ml

EXERCISE 6

1. Add.

    (a) 1 L 400 ml + 350 ml = _____ L _____ ml

    400 ml + 350 ml = 750 ml

    (b) 2 L 450 ml + 550 ml = _____ L _____ ml

    (c) 3 L 750 ml + 400 ml = _____ L _____ ml

    (d) 4 L 850 ml + 640 ml = _____ L _____ ml

2. Add.

    (a) 1 L 340 ml + 2 L 420 ml = _____ L _____ ml

    1 L 340 ml $\xrightarrow{+2 L}$ 3 L 340 ml $\xrightarrow{+420 ml}$ 3 L 760 ml

    (b) 2 L 250 ml + 1 L 640 ml = _____ L _____ ml

    (c) 3 L 670 ml + 1 L 400 ml = _____ L _____ ml

    (d) 3 L 85 ml + 2 L 960 ml = _____ L _____ ml

    (e) 4 L 706 ml + 3 L 308 ml = _____ L _____ ml

3. Subtract.

    (a) 3 L 740 ml − 560 ml = _____ L _____ ml

    740 ml − 560 ml = 180 ml

    (b) 4 L 820 ml − 780 ml = _____ L _____ ml

    (c) 5 L 30 ml − 360 ml = _____ L _____ ml

    (d) 6 L − 50 ml = _____ L _____ ml

4. Subtract.

    (a) 3 L 830 ml − 1 L 650 ml = _____ L _____ ml

    3 L 830 ml $\xrightarrow{-1\,L}$ 2 L 830 ml $\xrightarrow{-650\,ml}$ 2 L 180 ml

    (b) 2 L 824 ml − 1 L 760 ml = _____ L _____ ml

    (c) 4 L 40 ml − 1 L 375 ml = _____ L _____ ml

    (d) 3 L 150 ml − 2 L 390 ml = _____ L _____ ml

    (e) 9 L 5 ml − 3 L 284 ml = _____ L _____ ml

EXERCISE 7

Fill in the blanks.

1. The jug and the water bottle are filled with water.

 3 L    1 L 50 ml

(a) The jug holds _____ L _____ ml more water than the water bottle.

(b) The total capacity of the two containers is

_____ L _____ ml.

2. Cameron bought 3 cans of paint.

 5 L    2 L    3 L

A   B   C

(a) Can A contained _____ L more paint than Can C.

(b) The total capacity of the 3 cans was _____ L.

(c) Cameron used 8 L 400 ml of paint to paint his house. He had _____ L _____ ml of paint left.

3. Mr. Bill bought some fruit punch.
   He served 56 L of fruit punch to his customers.
   He had 27 L left.
   How many liters of fruit punch did he buy?

---

4. Rizal made 920 ml of milkshake.
   He poured it equally into 5 glasses.
   How much milkshake was there in each glass?

---

5. A can contains 250 ml of soda.
   Janet empties 6 cans of soda into a container to fill it
   completely.
   What is the capacity of the container? Give the answer in
   liters and milliliters.

6. There is 375 ml of milk in a carton.
   What is the total amount of milk in 6 cartons?
   Give the answer in liters and milliliters.

7. Deborah bought 4 cans of paint.
   Each can contained 3 L of paint.
   After painting her house, she had 2 L 450 ml of paint left.
   How much paint did she use for painting her house?

EXERCISE 8

Fill in the blanks.

1.

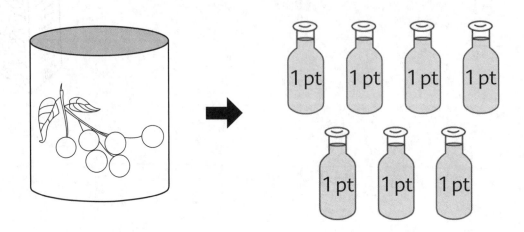

(a) The container can hold _____ pt of water.

(b) The capacity of the container is _____ pt.

2.

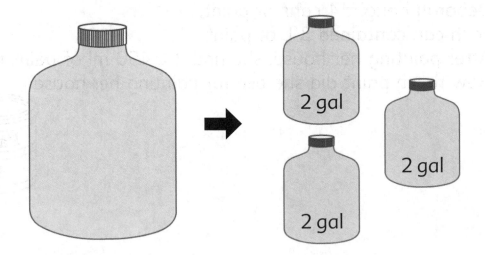

(a) The bottle can hold _____ gal of water.

(b) The capacity of the bottle is _____ gal.

3. The capacity of a tank is 250 gal.
   It contains 105 gal of water.
   How many more gallons of water are needed to fill the tank?

---

4. Check (✓) the statements that make sense.

   (a) A medicine bottle holds less than 1 c. ☐

   (b) The capacity of Stacy's mug is 1 qt. ☐

   (c) The kitchen sink holds 20 gal of water. ☐

   (d) Saul bought 2 qt of ice cream. ☐

   (e) Kristin and Lisa shared 1 pt of juice. ☐

   (f) Evie used 1 qt of milk to make a cake. ☐

   (g) A tea kettle holds about 8 c of water. ☐

   (h) The capacity of a bathtub is 24 c. ☐

EXERCISE 9

1. Match.

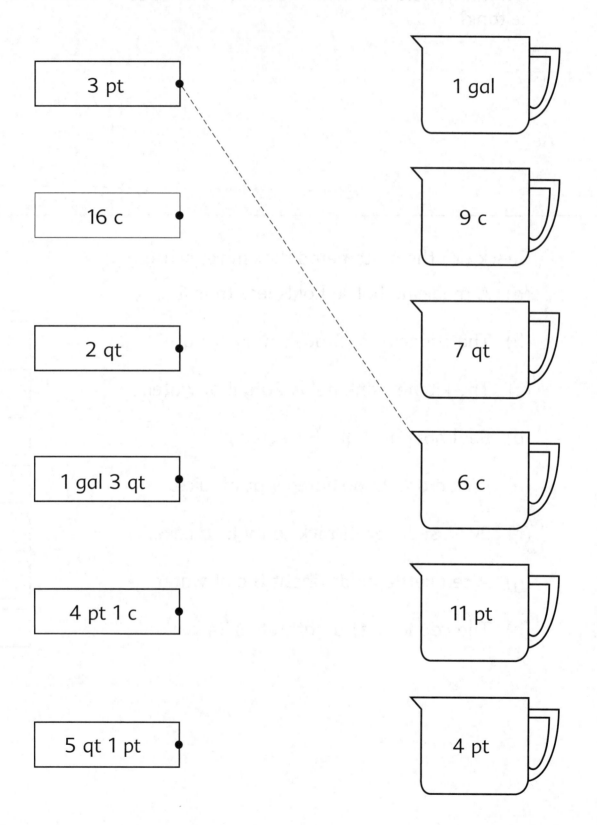

2. Fill in each ◯ with >, <, or =.

   (a) 2 gal 2 qt ◯ 10 qt   (b) 18 c ◯ 1 gal

   (c) 7 pt 1 c ◯ 16 c   (d) 26 qt ◯ 6 gal 1 qt

3. Arrange the following from the smallest to the greatest amount.

   4 pt 1 c   20 c   1 gal 2 c   1 qt

---

4. Lauren poured 4 gal of orange juice equally into 8 jugs.

   (a) How many quarts of orange juice were there in each jug?

   (b) How many cups of orange juice were there in each jug?

EXERCISE 10

1. Add or subtract.

   (a) 1 gal − 3 qt = _____ qt

   (b) 3 gal − 2 qt = _____ gal _____ qt

   (c) 3 qt + 2 qt = _____ gal _____ qt

   (d) 4 gal 2 qt + 3 qt = _____ gal _____ qt

   (e) 1 qt − 3 c = _____ c

   (f) 1 gal − 10 c = _____ c

2. Add in compound units.

   (a) 4 qt 3 c + 5 qt 1 c = _____ qt _____ c

   (b) 6 gal 3 qt + 8 gal 3 qt = _____ gal _____ qt

3. Subtract in compound units.

   (a) 4 gal 1 qt − 2 gal 3 qt = _____ gal _____ qt

   (b) 25 qt − 18 qt 1 pt = _____ qt _____ pt

4. Tank A and Tank B are filled with water.

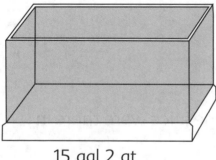

   15 gal 2 qt   6 gal 3 qt

   (a) Tank A holds _____ gal _____ qt more water
       than Tank B.

   (b) The total capacity of the two tanks is _____ gal
       _____ qt.

REVIEW 7

1. Fill in the blanks with **L** or **ml**.

   (a) The capacity of a cup is 200 _____.

   (b) Emily bought a kettle that can hold 3 _____ of water.

2. Fill in the blanks.

   (a) 3 L 60 ml = _____ ml

   (b) 4,105 ml = _____ L _____ ml

   (c) 2 L 480 ml = _____ ml

   (d) 6,005 ml = _____ L _____ ml

3. Add or subtract.

   (a) 4 L 380 ml + 1 L 275 ml = _____ L _____ ml

   (b) 3 L 600 ml − 2 L 290 ml = _____ L _____ ml

   (c) 4 L 865 ml + 3 L 750 ml = _____ L _____ ml

   (d) 5 L 50 ml − 2 L 90 ml = _____ L _____ ml

4. Fill in the blanks.

   (a) 4 gal 2 qt = _____ pt

   (b) 17 pt = _____ qt _____ pt

   (c) 5 gal 3 qt = _____ c

   (d) 28 qt = _____ gal _____ qt

5. Add or subtract.

   (a) 6 gal 3 qt + 21 gal 3 qt = _____ gal _____ qt

   (b) 12 gal 1 qt − 7 gal 2 qt = _____ gal _____ qt

   (c) 40 qt − 13 qt 2 c = _____ qt _____ c

   (d) 70 pt − 38 pt 1 c = _____ pt _____ c

6. Fill in each ◯ with **>**, **<**, or **=**.

   (a)   3 pt ◯ 7 c   (b)   8 pt 1 c ◯ 18 c

   (c)   33 c ◯ 2 gal   (d)   30 qt ◯ 7 gal 2 qt

7. Fill in the blanks.

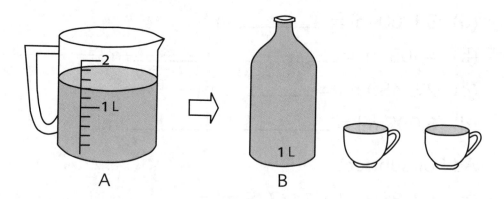

   A   B

   (a)   Jug A contains _____ L _____ ml of water.

   (b)   The capacity of Bottle B is _____.

   (c)   The water in Jug A fills up Bottle B and the two cups.
           The capacity of each cup is _____.

Fill in the blanks.

8.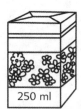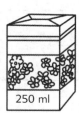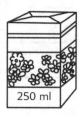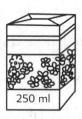

   250 ml   250 ml   250 ml   250 ml   250 ml   250 ml

   6 × 250 ml = _____ L _____ ml

9. A tank contains 17 gal of water.
   25 more gallons of water are needed to fill it.
   What is the capacity of the tank?

_____

10. A full tank holds 26 gal of water.
    It is emptied into buckets with a capacity of
    3 gal each.
    How many buckets are needed to empty the tank?

_____

11. Chef Thomas bought 2 L 100 ml of cooking oil.
    He used 750 ml of it to fry some eggs.
    How much cooking oil does he have left?
    Give your answer in liters and milliliters.

12. Tank A has a capacity of 3 L 150 ml.
Tank B has a capacity of 1 L 900 ml more than Tank A.

(a) What is the capacity of Tank B?
(b) What is the total capacity of both tanks?

Give your answers in liters and milliliters.

---

13. Pauline bought 8 cans of spray paint.
Each can contained 550 ml of spray paint.
She used 2 L 360 ml of spray paint for the classroom walls.

(a) How much spray paint did she buy?
(b) How much spray paint was left?

Give your answers in liters and milliliters.

EXERCISE 1

1. How much money is there in each purse?

    (a)

    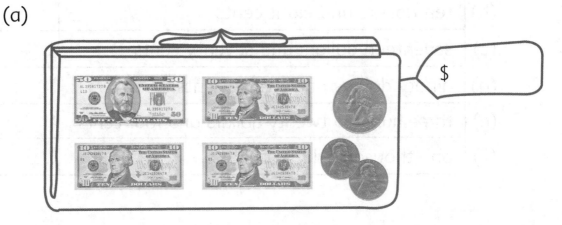

    $

    (b)

    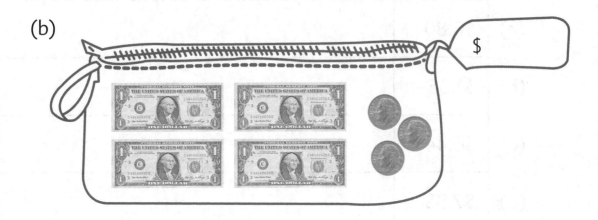

    $

    (c)

    $

2. Write each amount of money in figures.

(a)	five dollars and sixty-five cents	
(b)	ten dollars and eight cents	
(c)	seventeen dollars and seventy cents	
(d)	ninety dollars and twelve cents	
(e)	three hundred twenty dollars and four cents	
(f)	one thousand thirty dollars	

3. Write each amount of money in words.

(a)	$0.80	
(b)	$1.36	
(c)	$6.44	
(d)	$7.98	
(e)	$23.20	
(f)	$10.05	
(g)	$44.55	
(h)	$412	
(i)	$3,709	

EXERCISE 2

1. Write the missing numbers.

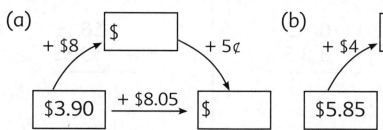

(a)

+ $8 → $ [ ]   + 5¢

$3.90 — + $8.05 → $ [ ]

(b)

+ $4 → $ [ ]   + 40¢

$5.85 — + $4.40 → $ [ ]

(c)

+ $6 → $ [ ]   + 75¢

$28.35 — + $6.75 → $ [ ]

(d)

+ $20 → $ [ ]   + 85¢

$46.35 — + $20.85 → $ [ ]

2. Add.

(a) $24.05 + $7.25 =	(b) $30.60 + $4.50 =
(c) $56.35 + $12.80 =	(d) $12.85 + $40.55 =

3. Add.

(a)

$$\begin{array}{r} 6\ 1\ 5 \\ +\ \ 3\ 8\ 5 \\ \hline \end{array}$$

$$\begin{array}{r} \$6.15 \\ +\ \ \$3.85 \\ \hline \end{array}$$

(b)

$$\begin{array}{r} 2,3\ 5\ 5 \\ +\ \ \ \ \ 7\ 6\ 0 \\ \hline \end{array}$$

$$\begin{array}{r} \$23.55 \\ +\ \ \$\ \ 7.60 \\ \hline \end{array}$$

(c)

$$\begin{array}{r} 3,0\ 9\ 0 \\ +\ \ 6,3\ 9\ 5 \\ \hline \end{array}$$

$$\begin{array}{r} \$30.90 \\ +\ \ \$63.95 \\ \hline \end{array}$$

(d)

$$\begin{array}{r} 7,3\ 1\ 5 \\ +\ \ 2,6\ 8\ 5 \\ \hline \end{array}$$

$$\begin{array}{r} \$73.15 \\ +\ \ \$26.85 \\ \hline \end{array}$$

4. Add.

$3.80 + $1.15 A	$7.40 + $8.95 E	$11.55 + $ 6.05 G
$31.53 + $48.76 I	$56.39 + $37.34 L	$78.22 + $ 6.98 N
$ 9.85 + $34.00 R	$10.05 + $43.09 S	$49.55 + $24.35 T

What can you get by dividing a square into halves?

Write the letters that match the answers to find out.

			A					
$73.90	$43.85	$80.29	$4.95	$85.20	$17.60	$93.73	$16.35	$53.14

EXERCISE 3

1. Complete the bills.

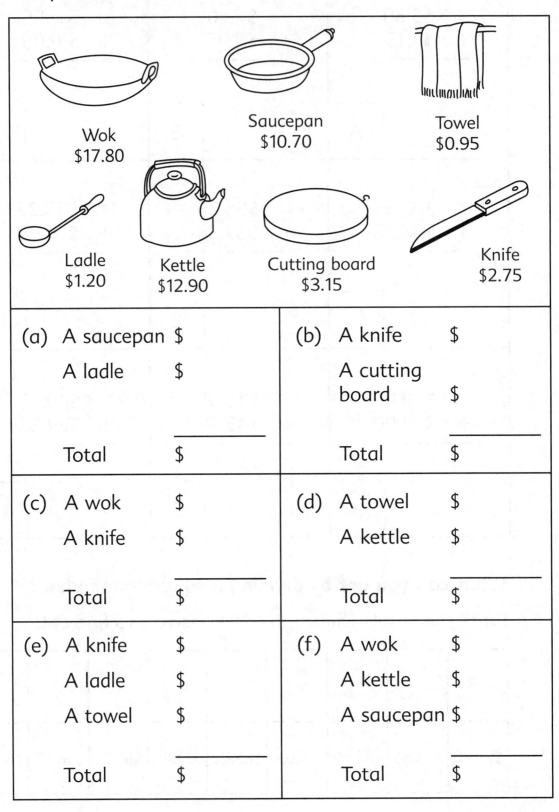

Wok
$17.80

Saucepan
$10.70

Towel
$0.95

Ladle
$1.20

Kettle
$12.90

Cutting board
$3.15

Knife
$2.75

(a)	A saucepan	$	(b)	A knife	$
	A ladle	$		A cutting board	$
	Total	$		Total	$

(c)	A wok	$	(d)	A towel	$
	A knife	$		A kettle	$
	Total	$		Total	$

(e)	A knife	$	(f)	A wok	$
	A ladle	$		A kettle	$
	A towel	$		A saucepan	$
	Total	$		Total	$

2. Mr. Williams has $42.65 in the bank.
   He deposits another $31.85.
   How much money does he have in the bank now?

---

3. Jim has $18.15.
   He needs $46.85 more to buy an electric iron.
   What is the cost of the iron?

---

4. A set of speakers costs $59.90.
   It costs $38.75 less than an e-book reader.
   What is the cost of the e-book reader?

EXERCISE 4

1. Write the missing numbers.

   (a)

   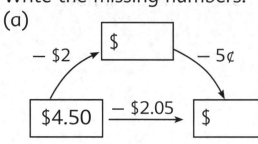

   (b)

   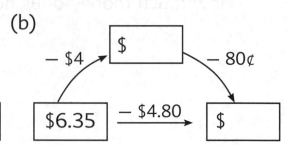

   (c)

   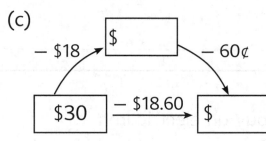

   (d)

   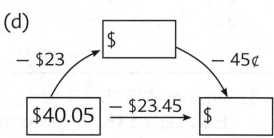

2. Subtract.

(a) $14.20 − $9.05 =	(b) $7.20 − $3.15 =
(c) $62.30 − $8.70 =	(d) $80 − $26.45 =

3. Subtract.

(a)

$$5,640 - 390$$

$$\$56.40 - \$\ 3.90$$

(b)

$$4,280 - 1,755$$

$$\$42.80 - \$17.55$$

(c)

$$6,005 - 1,485$$

$$\$60.05 - \$14.85$$

(d)

$$5,000 - 1,485$$

$$\$50.00 - \$14.85$$

4. Subtract.

$64.60 − $27.40	$50.00 − $24.50	$60.05 − $43.90
$70.50 − $ 7.05	$20.05 − $ 3.50	$32.00 − $24.99
$41.30 − $ 5.35	$25.60 − $ 9.75	$27.80 − $17.90

What is Jack's favorite game?

Color the letters that contain the answers above
to find out.

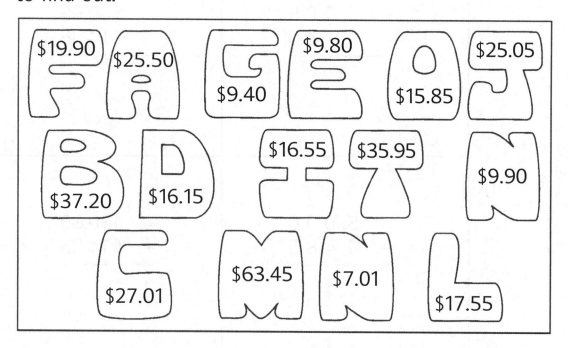

F $19.90
A $25.50
G $9.40
E $9.80
O $15.85
J $25.05
B $37.20
D $16.15
I $16.55
T $35.95
N $9.90
S $27.01
M $63.45
N $7.01
L $17.55

EXERCISE 5

1. Complete the table.

	I had	I bought	The amount of money left
(a)	$5	Baby's Birthday $2.75	
(b)	$1 $1 $1	$1.65	
(c)	$10 $10 50¢	$19.50	
(d)	$50 5¢ 10¢ 10¢	$24.80	
(e)	$50 $1 $20 $1	$69.90	

2. Warner bought a watch and a calculator for $60.25.
   The calculator cost $16.90.
   How much did the watch cost?

---

3. Kenneth spent $48.60 at a supermarket.
   He spent $3.55 more than Tasha.
   How much did Tasha spend?

---

4. The usual price of a watch is $70.
   At a sale, it is sold for $47.95.
   How much cheaper is the watch at the sale?

5. Helen bought a pair of shoes for $24.95.
   She also bought a shirt for $9.50.
   She gave the shopkeeper $50.
   How much change did she receive?

6. Stephanie bought a ball and a bat.
   The ball cost $1.20.
   The bat cost $2.60 more than the ball.
   How much did she spend altogether?

7. Mary bought a pen and a book.
   She gave the cashier $10 and received $2.05 change.
   The book cost $7.35.
   How much did the pen cost?

---

8. Sam spent $3.80 on breakfast.
   He spent $1.15 less on lunch than on breakfast.
   He had no money left.
   How much money did he have at first?

REVIEW 8

1. Write each amount of money in figures.

(a)	Three dollars and sixty cents	
(b)	Seventeen dollars and fourteen cents	
(c)	Forty-four dollars and ninety-five cents	
(d)	Sixty-eight dollars and twenty cents	

2. Write each amount of money in words.

(a)	$2.85	
(b)	$57.40	
(c)	$63.05	
(d)	$82.75	

3. Match the amounts.

(a) $0.70•   •$0.06

(b) 6¢•   • $4.05

(c) $9.35 •   •890¢

(d) 405¢•   •$6.55

(e) $8.90•   • 70¢

(f) 655¢•   •935¢

4. Fill in the blanks.

(a) 65¢ + _____ = $1

(b) _____ + 45¢ = $1

(c) $0.70 + _____ = $1

(d) _____ + $0.85 = $1

5. Draw a line to join each pair of amounts that makes $10. If you do it correctly, you will separate the apples from one another.

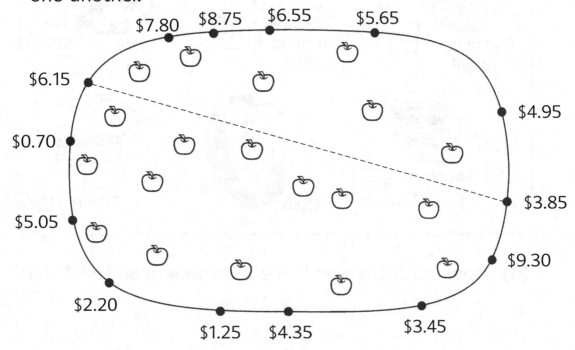

6. Add or subtract.

(a) $18.90 + $26.05 =	(b) $59.80 + $36.70 =
(c) $72.65 + $14.35 =	(d) $65.25 + $24.90 =
(e) $29.75 − $6.20 =	(f) $37.30 − $29.80 =
(g) $98.30 − $59.90 =	(h) $83.05 − $41.35 =

7.

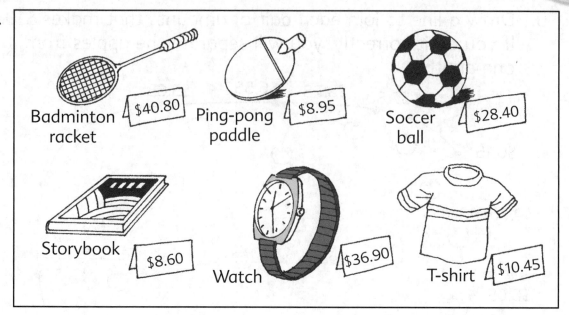

Badminton racket $40.80
Ping-pong paddle $8.95
Soccer ball $28.40
Storybook $8.60
Watch $36.90
T-shirt $10.45

(a) How much cheaper is the storybook than the T-shirt?

(b) Gary bought the ping-pong paddle, the badminton racket, and the soccer ball.
How much did he spend altogether?

(c) Cindy bought a watch, a book, and a T-shirt.
She gave the cashier $60.
How much change did she receive?

8. Jim has $25.40.
   He needs $34.60 more to buy a watch.
   How much does the watch cost?

---

9. Helen spent $70.25 at a souvenir store.
   She spent $35.60 more than Betty.
   How much did Betty spend at the souvenir store?

---

10. A pillow and a bedsheet set cost $71.65.
    The pillow costs $30.85.
    How much does the bedsheet cost?

11. Wayne saved $54.50 last week.
    He saved $18.90 less this week than last week.
    How much did he save altogether?

---

12. Mr. Frost bought a pair of shoes and a set of speakers.
    He gave the cashier $100 and he received change of
    $17.05.
    The pair of shoes cost $45.65.
    How much did the set of speakers cost?

EXERCISE 1

1. Fill in the blanks.
   The bar is divided into 4 equal parts.
   3 parts are shaded.

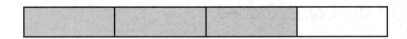

   (a) $\frac{3}{4}$ of the bar is shaded.

   $\frac{3}{4}$ is _____ out of the _____ equal parts.

   (b) 1 whole = _____ quarters

   $\frac{3}{4}$ = _____ quarters

   (c) $\frac{3}{4}$ and _____ make 1 whole.

2. Fill in the blanks.
   The bar is divided into 6 equal parts.
   4 parts are shaded.

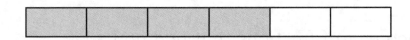

   (a) $\frac{4}{6}$ of the bar is shaded.

   $\frac{4}{6}$ is _____ out of the _____ equal parts.

   (b) 1 whole = _____ sixths

   $\frac{4}{6}$ = _____ sixths

   (c) $\frac{4}{6}$ and _____ make 1 whole.

3. Fill in the blanks.
   The bar is divided into 10 equal parts. 3 parts are shaded.

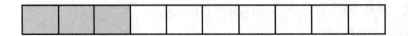

(a) $\frac{3}{10}$ of the bar is shaded.

   $\frac{3}{10}$ is _____ out of the _____ equal parts.

(b) 1 whole = _____ tenths

   $\frac{3}{10}$ = _____ tenths

(c) $\frac{3}{10}$ and _____ make 1 whole.

4. Write the missing fractions.

(a) $\frac{4}{5}$ and _____ make 1 whole.

(b) $\frac{5}{9}$ and _____ make 1 whole.

5. Join each pair of fractions that add up to 1.

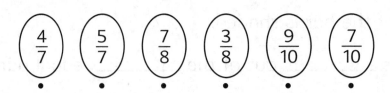

6. Complete the following.

(a)
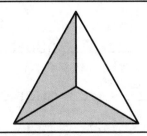
$\frac{1}{3} + \frac{1}{3} =$

2 thirds

(b)
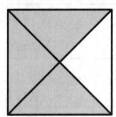
$\frac{1}{4} + \frac{1}{4} + \frac{1}{4} =$

3 quarters

(c)
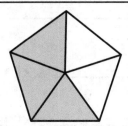
$\frac{1}{5} + \frac{1}{5} + \frac{1}{5} =$

3 fifths

(d)
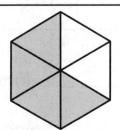
$\frac{1}{6} + \frac{1}{6} + \frac{1}{6} + \frac{1}{6} =$

4 sixths

(e)
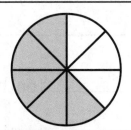
$\frac{1}{8} + \frac{1}{8} + \frac{1}{8} + \frac{1}{8} + \frac{1}{8} =$

5 eighths

(f)
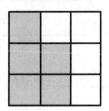
$\frac{1}{9} + \frac{1}{9} + \frac{1}{9} + \frac{1}{9} + \frac{1}{9} =$

5 ninths

7. Complete the following.

(a)

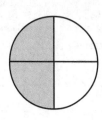

$1 = \underline{\hspace{2cm}}$ quarters $= \dfrac{}{4}$

$\dfrac{2}{4} = \underline{\hspace{2cm}}$ quarters

(b)

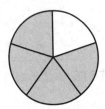

$1 = \underline{\hspace{2cm}}$ fifths $= \dfrac{}{5}$

$\dfrac{4}{5} = \underline{\hspace{2cm}}$ fifths

(c)

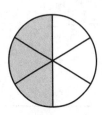

$1 = \underline{\hspace{2cm}}$ sixths $= \dfrac{}{6}$

$\dfrac{3}{6} = \underline{\hspace{2cm}}$ sixths

(d)

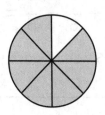

$1 = \underline{\hspace{2cm}}$ eighths $= \dfrac{}{8}$

$\dfrac{7}{8} = \underline{\hspace{2cm}}$ eighths

(e)

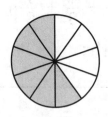

$1 = \underline{\hspace{2cm}}$ tenths $= \dfrac{}{10}$

$\dfrac{6}{10} = \underline{\hspace{2cm}}$ tenths

(f)

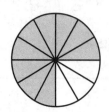

$1 = \underline{\hspace{2cm}}$ twelfths $= \dfrac{}{12}$

$\dfrac{9}{12} = \underline{\hspace{2cm}}$ twelfths

8. What fraction of each circle is shaded?
   Match the circles to the correct answers.

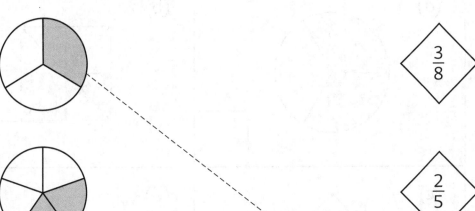

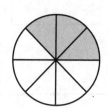

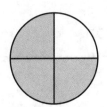

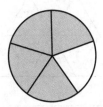

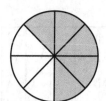

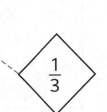

9. What fraction of each figure is shaded?

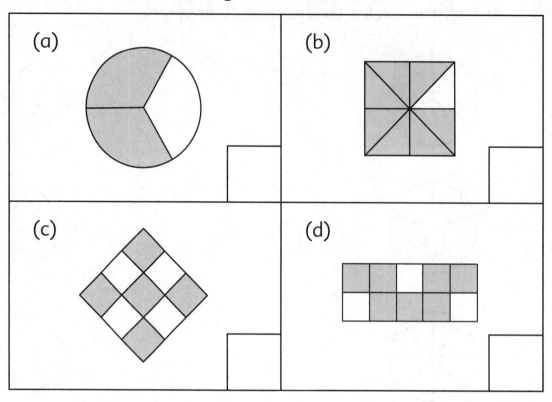

(a)

(b)

(c)

(d)

10. Color each figure to show the given fraction.

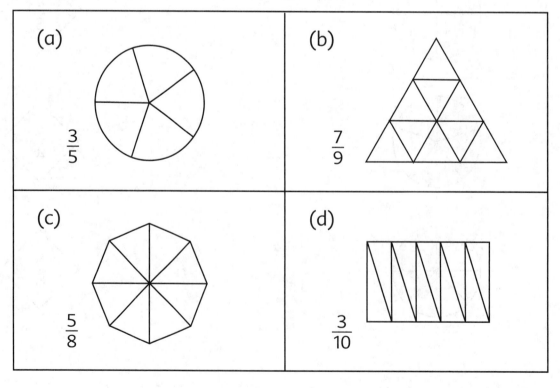

(a) $\frac{3}{5}$

(b) $\frac{7}{9}$

(c) $\frac{5}{8}$

(d) $\frac{3}{10}$

EXERCISE 2

1. Circle the greater fraction.

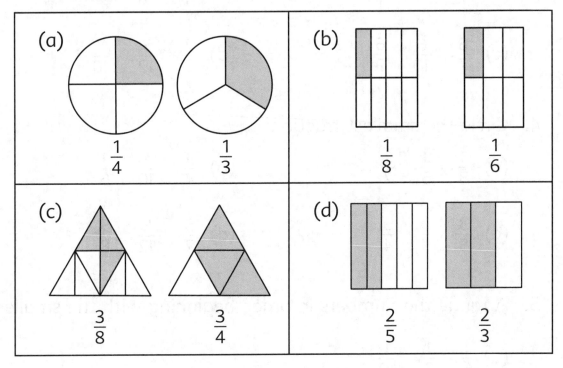

(a) $\dfrac{1}{4}$ $\dfrac{1}{3}$

(b) $\dfrac{1}{8}$ $\dfrac{1}{6}$

(c) $\dfrac{3}{8}$ $\dfrac{3}{4}$

(d) $\dfrac{2}{5}$ $\dfrac{2}{3}$

2. Circle the smaller fraction.

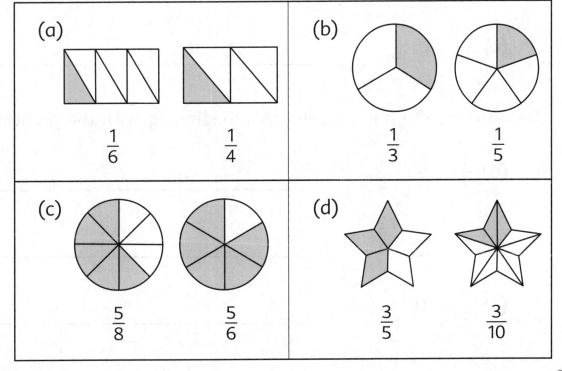

(a) $\dfrac{1}{6}$ $\dfrac{1}{4}$

(b) $\dfrac{1}{3}$ $\dfrac{1}{5}$

(c) $\dfrac{5}{8}$ $\dfrac{5}{6}$

(d) $\dfrac{3}{5}$ $\dfrac{3}{10}$

3. Circle the greatest fraction.

(a) $\frac{1}{12}$, $\frac{1}{7}$, $\frac{1}{10}$

(b) $\frac{1}{11}$, $\frac{1}{8}$, $\frac{1}{9}$

(c) $\frac{6}{7}$, $\frac{6}{10}$, $\frac{6}{9}$

(d) $\frac{7}{8}$, $\frac{7}{12}$, $\frac{7}{10}$

4. Circle the smallest fraction.

(a) $\frac{1}{3}$, $\frac{1}{5}$, $\frac{1}{2}$

(b) $\frac{1}{4}$, $\frac{1}{10}$, $\frac{1}{6}$

(c) $\frac{3}{5}$, $\frac{3}{7}$, $\frac{3}{4}$

(d) $\frac{5}{7}$, $\frac{5}{12}$, $\frac{5}{8}$

5. Arrange the numbers in order, beginning with the smallest.

(a) $\frac{1}{6}$, $\frac{1}{7}$, $\frac{1}{10}$ _____

(b) $\frac{3}{4}$, $\frac{3}{10}$, $\frac{3}{8}$ _____

(c) $\frac{1}{5}$, 1, $\frac{1}{9}$ _____

6. Arrange the numbers in order, beginning with the greatest.

(a) $\frac{1}{4}$, $\frac{1}{12}$, $\frac{1}{3}$ _____

(b) $\frac{5}{7}$, $\frac{5}{12}$, $\frac{5}{9}$ _____

(c) $\frac{1}{10}$, 0, $\frac{1}{8}$ _____

7. Write the missing numbers in the following regular number patterns.

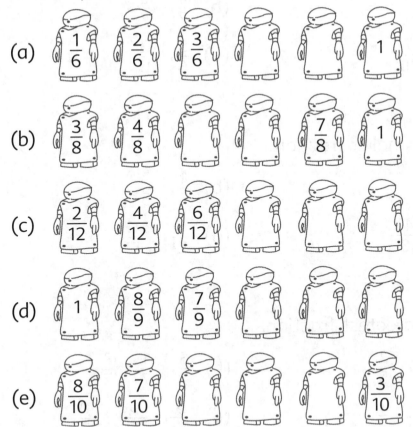

(a) $\frac{1}{6}$ $\frac{2}{6}$ $\frac{3}{6}$ ☐ ☐ 1

(b) $\frac{3}{8}$ $\frac{4}{8}$ ☐ ☐ $\frac{7}{8}$ 1

(c) $\frac{2}{12}$ $\frac{4}{12}$ $\frac{6}{12}$ ☐ ☐ ☐

(d) 1 $\frac{8}{9}$ $\frac{7}{9}$ ☐ ☐ ☐

(e) $\frac{8}{10}$ $\frac{7}{10}$ ☐ ☐ ☐ $\frac{3}{10}$

8. Circle the greater fraction.

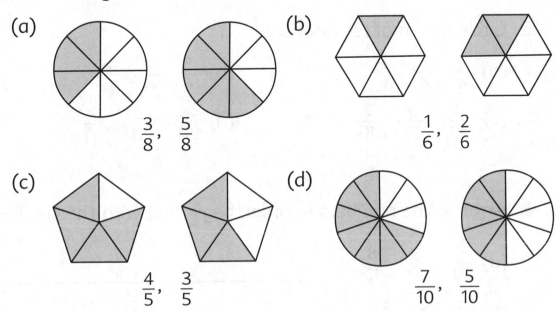

(a) $\frac{3}{8}$, $\frac{5}{8}$

(b) $\frac{1}{6}$, $\frac{2}{6}$

(c) $\frac{4}{5}$, $\frac{3}{5}$

(d) $\frac{7}{10}$, $\frac{5}{10}$

9. Circle the greater fraction.

(a) $\frac{4}{5}$, $\frac{1}{5}$

(b) $\frac{4}{7}$, $\frac{6}{7}$

(c) $\frac{3}{10}$, $\frac{7}{10}$

(d) $\frac{5}{6}$, $\frac{3}{6}$

10. Circle the smaller fraction.

(a) $\frac{2}{3}$, $\frac{1}{3}$

(b) $\frac{1}{5}$, $\frac{3}{5}$

(c) $\frac{9}{10}$, $\frac{4}{10}$

(d) $\frac{5}{12}$, $\frac{11}{12}$

11. Circle the greatest fraction.

(a) $\frac{1}{5}$, $\frac{4}{5}$, $\frac{2}{5}$

(b) $\frac{6}{7}$, $\frac{1}{7}$, $\frac{3}{7}$

(c) $\frac{5}{9}$, $\frac{8}{9}$, $\frac{2}{9}$

(d) $\frac{5}{12}$, $\frac{9}{12}$, $\frac{10}{12}$

12. Circle the smallest fraction.

(a) $\frac{1}{4}$, $\frac{3}{4}$, $\frac{2}{4}$

(b) $\frac{5}{6}$, $\frac{2}{6}$, $\frac{4}{6}$

(c) $\frac{4}{10}$, $\frac{9}{10}$, $\frac{7}{10}$

(d) $\frac{8}{11}$, $\frac{5}{11}$, $\frac{2}{11}$

13. Arrange the numbers in order, beginning with the smallest.

(a) $\frac{5}{10}$, $\frac{3}{10}$, $\frac{8}{10}$ _____

(b) $\frac{5}{12}$, 1, $\frac{3}{12}$ _____

14. Each of the following lines has been divided into equal parts. Fill in the missing fractions.

(a)

0   ☐   1

(b)

0   ☐   1

(c)

0   ☐   1

(d)

0   ☐   1

(e)

0   ☐   1

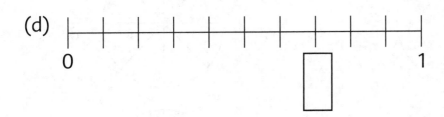

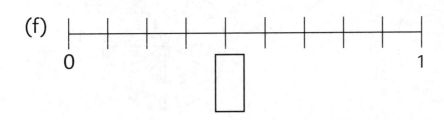

(f)

0   ☐   1

EXERCISE 3

1. Join each pair of equivalent fractions.

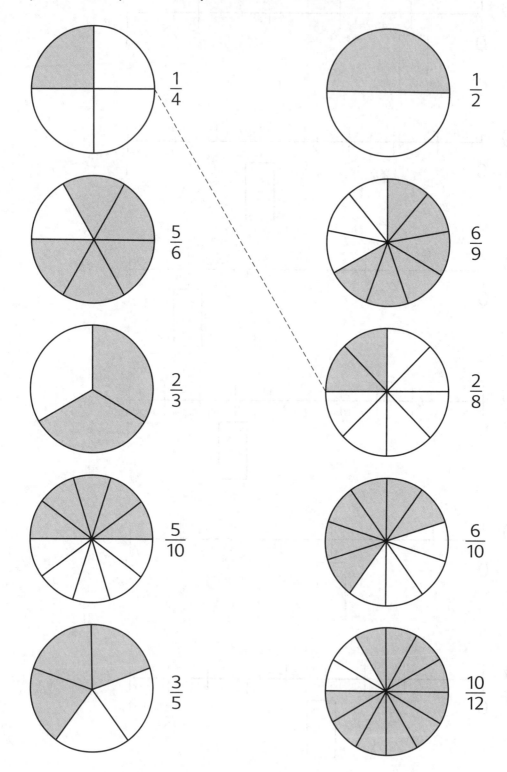

Unit 9: Fractions

2. Use the fraction bars to help you find the missing numerators.

$\dfrac{1}{2}$	$\dfrac{1}{2}$

$\dfrac{1}{3}$	$\dfrac{1}{3}$	$\dfrac{1}{3}$

$\dfrac{1}{4}$	$\dfrac{1}{4}$	$\dfrac{1}{4}$	$\dfrac{1}{4}$

$\dfrac{1}{5}$	$\dfrac{1}{5}$	$\dfrac{1}{5}$	$\dfrac{1}{5}$	$\dfrac{1}{5}$

$\dfrac{1}{6}$	$\dfrac{1}{6}$	$\dfrac{1}{6}$	$\dfrac{1}{6}$	$\dfrac{1}{6}$	$\dfrac{1}{6}$

$\dfrac{1}{8}$	$\dfrac{1}{8}$	$\dfrac{1}{8}$	$\dfrac{1}{8}$	$\dfrac{1}{8}$	$\dfrac{1}{8}$	$\dfrac{1}{8}$	$\dfrac{1}{8}$

$\dfrac{1}{10}$	$\dfrac{1}{10}$	$\dfrac{1}{10}$	$\dfrac{1}{10}$	$\dfrac{1}{10}$	$\dfrac{1}{10}$	$\dfrac{1}{10}$	$\dfrac{1}{10}$	$\dfrac{1}{10}$	$\dfrac{1}{10}$

(a) $\dfrac{1}{2} = \dfrac{}{4}$

(b) $\dfrac{1}{2} = \dfrac{}{6}$

(c) $\dfrac{1}{2} = \dfrac{}{10}$

(d) $\dfrac{1}{3} = \dfrac{}{6}$

(e) $\dfrac{2}{3} = \dfrac{}{6}$

(f) $\dfrac{3}{3} = \dfrac{}{10}$

(g) $\dfrac{1}{4} = \dfrac{}{8}$

(h) $\dfrac{2}{4} = \dfrac{}{8}$

(i) $\dfrac{3}{4} = \dfrac{}{8}$

(j) $\dfrac{1}{5} = \dfrac{}{10}$

(k) $\dfrac{2}{5} = \dfrac{}{10}$

(l) $\dfrac{4}{5} = \dfrac{}{10}$

3. Use the number lines to help you find the missing numerators.

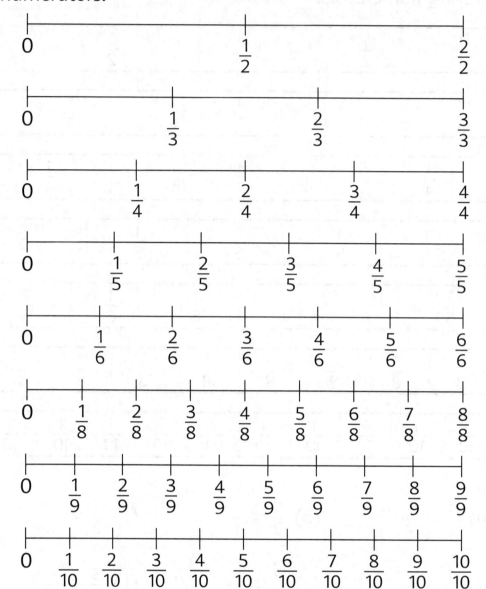

(a) $\dfrac{1}{3} = \dfrac{}{9}$

(b) $\dfrac{3}{4} = \dfrac{}{8}$

(c) $\dfrac{2}{5} = \dfrac{}{10}$

(d) $\dfrac{1}{2} = \dfrac{}{8}$

(e) $\dfrac{3}{5} = \dfrac{}{10}$

(f) $\dfrac{2}{3} = \dfrac{}{6}$

(g) $\dfrac{2}{3} = \dfrac{}{9}$

(h) $\dfrac{1}{2} = \dfrac{}{10}$

(i) $\dfrac{3}{3} = \dfrac{}{8}$

(j) $\dfrac{4}{8} = \dfrac{}{10}$

(k) $\dfrac{3}{6} = \dfrac{}{8}$

(l) $\dfrac{4}{6} = \dfrac{}{9}$

EXERCISE 4

1. Write the missing numerators and denominators.

(a)

 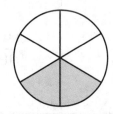 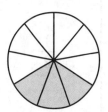

$$\frac{1}{3} \quad = \quad \frac{2}{} \quad = \quad \frac{}{9}$$

(b)

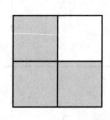 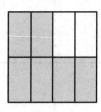 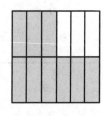

$$\frac{3}{4} \quad = \quad \frac{}{8} \quad = \quad \frac{9}{}$$

(c)

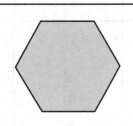 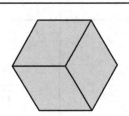 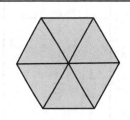

$$1 \quad = \quad \frac{}{3} \quad = \quad \frac{6}{}$$

2. Write the missing numerators and denominators.

(a) $\frac{4}{5}$ $\overset{\times\,2}{=}$ $\underset{\times\,2}{}$ ——

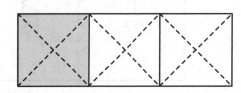

(b) $\frac{1}{3}$ $\overset{\times\,4}{=}$ $\underset{\times\,4}{}$ ——

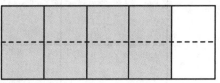

3. Circle eight pairs of equivalent fractions.
   One pair has been done for you.

$\frac{1}{2}$	$\frac{1}{5}$	$\frac{9}{10}$	$\frac{4}{5}$	$\frac{8}{10}$
$\frac{2}{4}$	$\frac{2}{12}$	$\frac{2}{10}$	$\frac{4}{10}$	$\frac{1}{4}$
$\frac{2}{6}$	$\frac{1}{3}$	$\frac{2}{3}$	$\frac{3}{8}$	$\frac{2}{8}$
$\frac{1}{6}$	$\frac{1}{2}$	$\frac{1}{12}$	$\frac{2}{6}$	$\frac{5}{9}$
$\frac{5}{10}$	$\frac{5}{6}$	$\frac{2}{9}$	$\frac{3}{9}$	$\frac{4}{9}$
$\frac{11}{12}$	$\frac{3}{5}$	$\frac{6}{10}$	$\frac{6}{7}$	$\frac{5}{7}$

EXERCISE 5

1. Write the equivalent fraction for each of the following.

(a)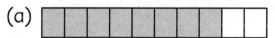

$\frac{8}{10} =$

(b)

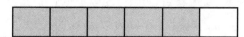

$\frac{10}{12} =$

(c)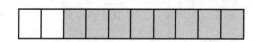

$\frac{6}{8} =$

(d)

$\frac{4}{5} =$

(e)

$\frac{5}{10} =$

(f)

$\frac{6}{9} =$

(g)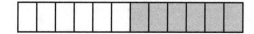

$\frac{2}{4} =$

(h)

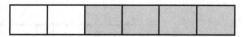

$\frac{4}{6} =$

2. Circle the equivalent fraction for each of the given fractions.

(a)	$\frac{2}{3}$	$\frac{3}{4}$	$\boxed{\frac{4}{6}}$	$\frac{5}{10}$
(b)	$\frac{4}{5}$	$\frac{2}{8}$	$\frac{3}{4}$	$\frac{8}{10}$
(c)	$\frac{4}{10}$	$\frac{2}{5}$	$\frac{5}{8}$	$\frac{6}{12}$
(d)	$\frac{3}{3}$	$\frac{4}{8}$	$\frac{6}{6}$	$\frac{8}{12}$
(e)	$\frac{9}{12}$	$\frac{2}{3}$	$\frac{3}{4}$	$\frac{6}{10}$
(f)	$\frac{1}{6}$	$\frac{1}{3}$	$\frac{2}{12}$	$\frac{3}{8}$
(g)	$\frac{6}{8}$	$\frac{2}{5}$	$\frac{3}{4}$	$\frac{8}{12}$
(h)	$\frac{1}{2}$	$\frac{2}{3}$	$\frac{6}{9}$	$\frac{5}{10}$

EXERCISE 6

1. Write the missing numerators and denominators.

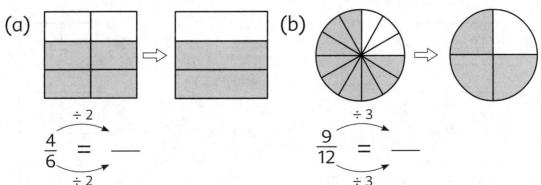

(a)

$$\frac{4}{6} \xrightarrow{\div 2} = \underline{\hspace{1cm}}$$

(b)

$$\frac{9}{12} \xrightarrow{\div 3} = \underline{\hspace{1cm}}$$

2. Write each fraction in its simplest form.

(a) $\frac{5}{10} = $ _____   (b) $\frac{6}{9} = $ _____   (c) $\frac{4}{12} = $ _____

3. Color the spaces in which the fraction is in its simplest form.
    You will find the name of Simon's dog.

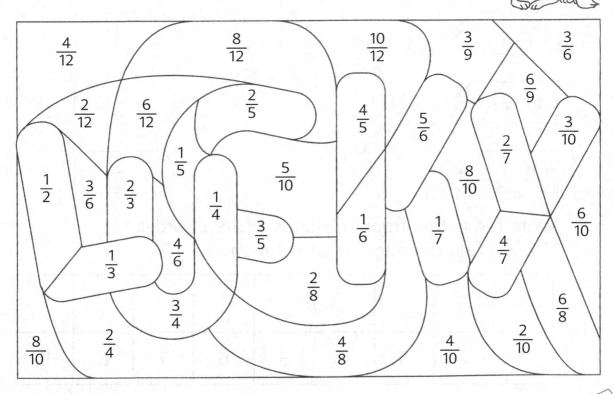

4. Join each pair of equivalent fractions with a straight line.
The line will pass through a letter.

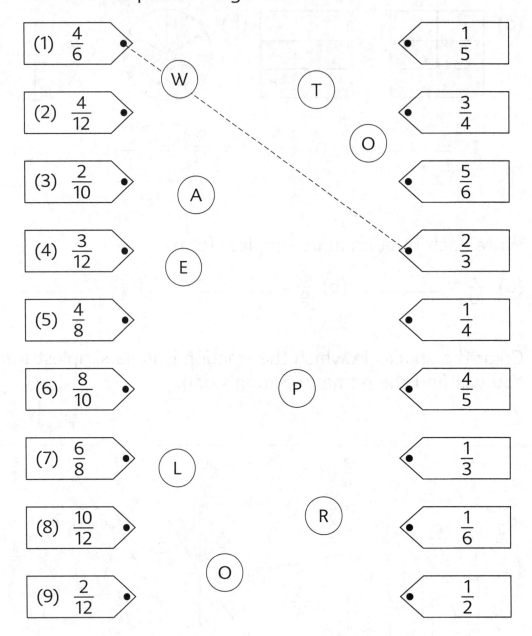

(1) $\frac{4}{6}$
(2) $\frac{4}{12}$
(3) $\frac{2}{10}$
(4) $\frac{3}{12}$
(5) $\frac{4}{8}$
(6) $\frac{8}{10}$
(7) $\frac{6}{8}$
(8) $\frac{10}{12}$
(9) $\frac{2}{12}$

W T O A E P L R O

$\frac{1}{5}$
$\frac{3}{4}$
$\frac{5}{6}$
$\frac{2}{3}$
$\frac{1}{4}$
$\frac{4}{5}$
$\frac{1}{3}$
$\frac{1}{6}$
$\frac{1}{2}$

Write the letters from questions 1 to 9 in order.
You will find the name of a water sport.

W								
1	2	3	4	5	6	7	8	9

EXERCISE 7

1. Circle the greater fraction.

   (a) $\frac{7}{8}$, $\frac{3}{4}$

   (b) $\frac{4}{5}$, $\frac{7}{10}$

   (c) $\frac{5}{9}$, $\frac{2}{3}$

   (d) $\frac{2}{3}$, $\frac{1}{6}$

   (e) $\frac{7}{10}$, $\frac{4}{5}$

   (f) $\frac{3}{4}$, $\frac{11}{12}$

   (g) $\frac{2}{3}$, $\frac{5}{12}$

   (h) $\frac{5}{12}$, $\frac{1}{2}$

Change to common denominators first.

2. Arrange the fractions in order, beginning with the smallest.

   (a) $\frac{2}{3}$, $\frac{1}{2}$, $\frac{5}{6}$ _____

   (b) $\frac{5}{8}$, $\frac{3}{4}$, $\frac{1}{2}$ _____

   (c) $\frac{7}{12}$, $\frac{5}{6}$, $\frac{2}{3}$ _____

   (d) $\frac{2}{3}$, $\frac{3}{4}$, $\frac{7}{12}$ _____

EXERCISE 8

1. Fill in the blanks.

    (a) Here are three strings, A, B, and C.

    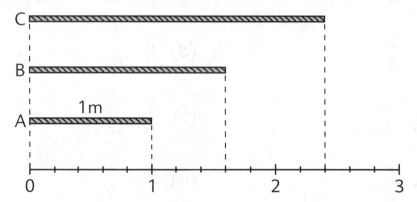

    The length of A is 1 m.

    The length of B is _____ m.

    The length of C is _____ m.

    (b)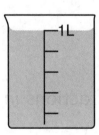

    The total amount of water is _____ L.

    (c)

    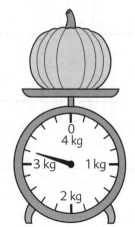

    The pumpkin weighs _____ kg.

2. How long is each string? Write the length in the simplest form.

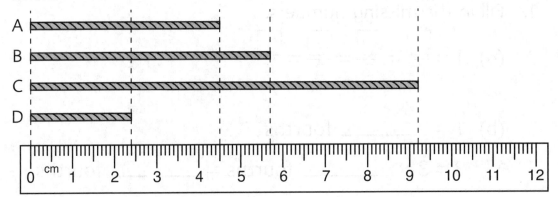

(a) String A is _____ cm long.

(b) String B is _____ cm long.

(c) String C is _____ cm long.

(d) String D is _____ cm long.

3. Measure the lines to the nearest eighth of an inch.
Write the length in the simplest form.

(a) ━━━━━━━━━━━━━━━━━━ _____ in.

(b) ━━━━━━━━━━━━━━━━━━━ _____ in.

(c) ━━━━━━━━━━━━━━━━━━━━━━ _____ in.

(d) ━━━━━━━━━━━━ _____ in.

(e) ━━━━ _____ in.

(f) ━━━━━━━━━━━━━━━━━━━━━━━ _____ in.

EXERCISE 9

1. Fill in the missing numbers.

    (a) $1 = \dfrac{\square}{1} = \dfrac{\square}{2} = \dfrac{\square}{3} = \dfrac{\square}{4}$

    (b) $1 = $ _____ fourths

    $3 = 3 \times$ _____ fourths $=$ _____ fourths

    (c) $1 = $ _____ eighths

    $5 = 5 \times$ _____ eighths $=$ _____ eighths

    (d) $4 = \dfrac{\square}{1} = \dfrac{\square}{2} = \dfrac{\square}{3} = \dfrac{\square}{4} = \dfrac{\square}{9}$

    (e) There are _____ sixths in 4.

2. Marie is laying tiles in a row along the edge of a hallway. Each tile is $\dfrac{1}{2}$ ft long.

   She has laid 8 ft of tile. How many tiles has she used?

   _____

3. John has a jar with a capacity of $\dfrac{1}{3}$ L and a pitcher with a capacity of 4 L.
   How many times does he need to fill the jar and pour it into the pitcher to fill the pitcher? _____

EXERCISE 10

1. Fill in the blanks.

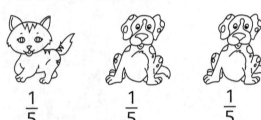

$\frac{1}{5}$ $\frac{1}{5}$ $\frac{1}{5}$ $\frac{1}{5}$ $\frac{1}{5}$

There are _____ equal parts.

_____ part is a kitten.

_____ parts are puppies.

$\frac{1}{5}$ of the pets is a kitten.

$\dfrac{\square}{\square}$ of the pets are puppies.

2. Write the fraction that shows the shaded part.

(a) 	There are 4 equal parts. The shaded part is $\dfrac{\square}{\square}$.
(b) ⬤ ⬤ ⬤ ◯ ◯ ◯ ◯ ◯	
(c) ⬤ ⬤ ◯ ◯ ◯ ◯ ◯ ◯ ◯	

3. Sherry found 5 lizards.
    2 of the lizards were striped and 3 were not striped.
    What fraction of the lizards were striped?

4. (a) What fraction of the kittens are sleeping?

    (b) What fraction of the kittens are awake?

5. Drake did 5 math problems.
    He got 1 wrong.
    What fraction of the problems did he get right?

EXERCISE 11

1. Find the missing numbers.
   (a) What fraction of the fruit is made up of apples?

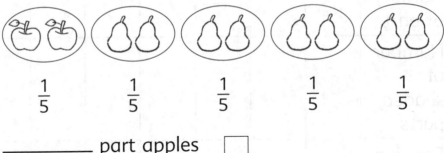

$$\frac{1}{5} \qquad \frac{1}{5} \qquad \frac{1}{5} \qquad \frac{1}{5} \qquad \frac{1}{5}$$

   _____ part apples
   _____ equal parts $= \dfrac{\square}{\square}$

   (b) What fraction of the fruit is pears? $\dfrac{\square}{\square}$

2. Write the fraction for the shaded part.

(a) 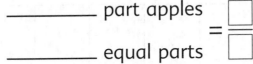	There are 4 equal parts. The shaded part is $\dfrac{\square}{\square}$.
(b)	
(c)	

3. What fraction of each set is shaded?

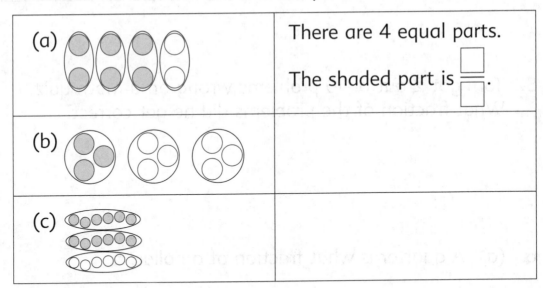

4. Complete the table.

Number of parts	12		12					
Number of shaded parts	0							
Fraction of shaded parts	$\dfrac{0}{12}$			$\dfrac{4}{12}$				
Simplest form	0							1

5. Tom got 2 out of 10 problems wrong on a math quiz. What fraction of the problems did he get correct?

6. (a) A quarter is what fraction of a dollar?

   (b) A dime is what fraction of a dollar?

REVIEW 9

1. Color each bar to show the given fraction.

$\frac{1}{4}$

$\frac{2}{4}$

$\frac{1}{6}$

$\frac{2}{3}$

$\frac{2}{8}$

2. Circle the greater fraction.
   (Use the fraction bars above to help you.)

   (a) $\frac{1}{4}$, $\frac{1}{6}$ (b) $\frac{1}{4}$, $\frac{3}{8}$ (c) $\frac{2}{8}$, $\frac{2}{3}$

   (d) $\frac{2}{4}$, $\frac{4}{6}$ (e) $\frac{2}{3}$, $\frac{3}{4}$ (f) $\frac{1}{3}$, $\frac{3}{8}$

3. Circle the smaller fraction.

   (a) $\frac{2}{5}$, $\frac{7}{10}$ (b) $\frac{5}{6}$, $\frac{1}{3}$

   (c) $\frac{5}{12}$, $\frac{3}{4}$ (d) $\frac{1}{2}$, $\frac{3}{8}$

4. Fill in each $\bigcirc$ with >, <, or =.

   (a) $\frac{4}{7}$ $\bigcirc$ $\frac{3}{7}$ (b) $\frac{3}{5}$ $\bigcirc$ $\frac{3}{8}$

   (c) $\frac{8}{2}$ $\bigcirc$ $\frac{12}{3}$ (d) $1\frac{3}{4}$ $\bigcirc$ $1\frac{4}{8}$

5. Write the missing numerators and denominators.

(a) $\dfrac{1}{5} = \dfrac{}{15} = \dfrac{2}{}$ (b) $\dfrac{3}{9} = \dfrac{9}{} = \dfrac{}{18}$ (c) $\dfrac{3}{9} = \dfrac{6}{} = \dfrac{}{12}$

6. Express each of the following in its simplest form.

(a) $\dfrac{8}{2}$ (b) $\dfrac{12}{4}$

(c) $1\dfrac{4}{8}$ (d) $\dfrac{8}{32}$

7. Write the fractions in order, beginning with the smallest.

(a) $\dfrac{1}{8}$, $\dfrac{7}{8}$, $\dfrac{4}{8}$ _____

(b) $\dfrac{5}{15}$, $\dfrac{4}{5}$, $\dfrac{2}{15}$ _____

(c) $\dfrac{2}{6}$, $\dfrac{2}{8}$, $\dfrac{1}{2}$ _____

8. Measure the lines to the tenth of a centimeter.
   Write the length in the simplest form.

(a)    _____ cm

(b)    _____ cm

(c)    _____ cm

(d)    _____ cm

(e)    _____ cm

9. 5 poles are placed $\frac{1}{2}$ m apart.

The distance from the first pole to
the last pole is about _____.

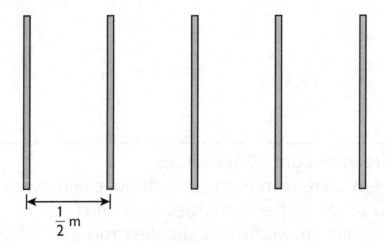

10. There are 3 red marbles and 5 yellow marbles.
    What fraction of the marbles is yellow?
    Express your answer in the simplest form.

11. Mr. Evan has 7 plants.
    4 of them have flowers but the rest do not.
    What fraction of his plants do not have flowers?
    Express your answer in the simplest form.

12. Amy has 8 birds.
    2 of them are parakeets.
    What fraction of her birds are parakeets?
    Express your answer in the simplest form.

_____

13. Mrs. Green bought 10 tomatoes.
    4 of them were rotten and she threw them away.
    What fraction of her tomatoes were left?
    Express your answer in the simplest form.

_____

14. Roger has 5 quarters, 5 dimes, and 5 nickels.
    What fraction of his coins are nickels?
    Express your answer in the simplest form.

EXERCISE 1

1. What time is shown on each clock?
   Match the clocks to the correct answers.

 4:36

7:17

 8:03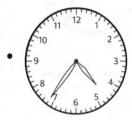

8:14

 2:41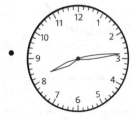

12:21

 4:02

11:52

2. What time is it?

7:30

or half past seven

5:24

24 minutes past 5

_____

_____

_____

or _____

_____

_____

_____

_____

_____

or _____

_____

_____

_____

_____

_____

or _____

_____

_____

EXERCISE 2

1. Complete the following.

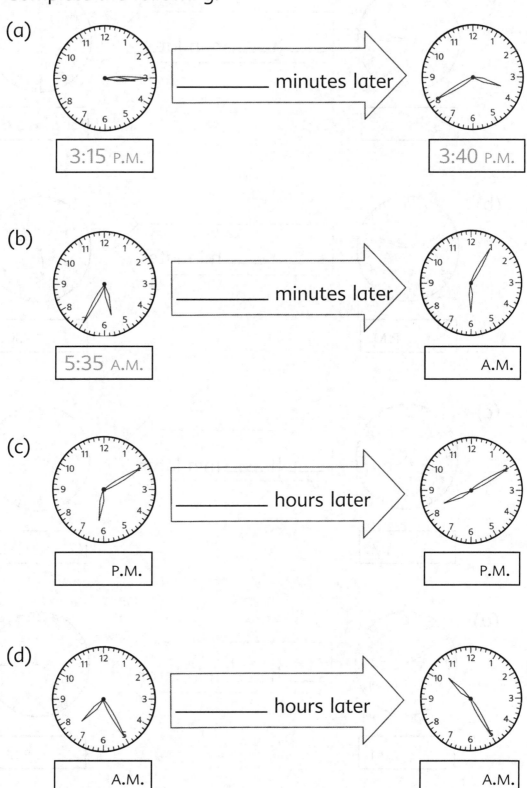

(a) 3:15 P.M. _____ minutes later 3:40 P.M.

(b) 5:35 A.M. _____ minutes later _____ A.M.

(c) _____ P.M. _____ hours later _____ P.M.

(d) _____ A.M. _____ hours later _____ A.M.

2. Complete the following.

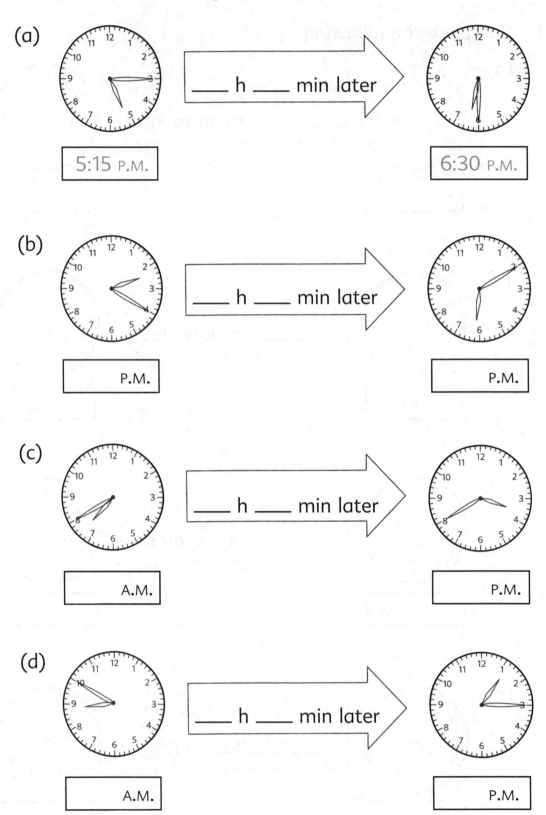

(a)

_____ h _____ min later

5:15 P.M.

6:30 P.M.

(b)

_____ h _____ min later

P.M.

P.M.

(c)

_____ h _____ min later

A.M.

P.M.

(d)

_____ h _____ min later

A.M.

P.M.

EXERCISE 3

1. Match.

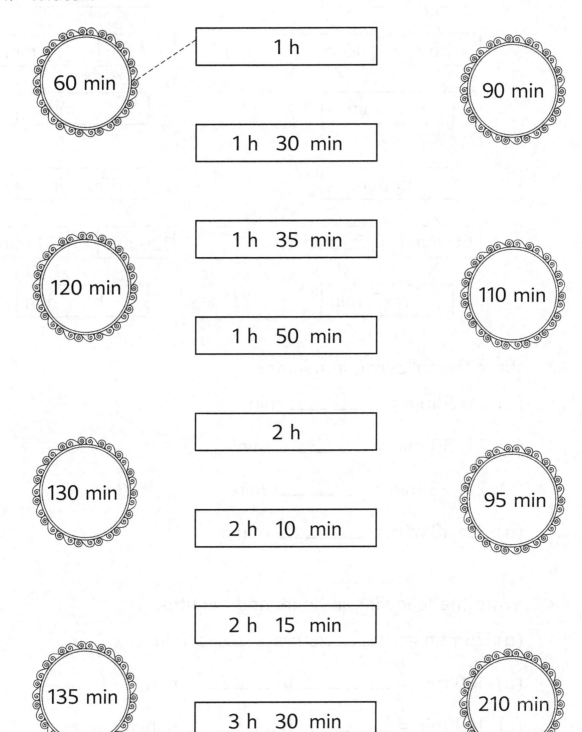

2. Write the missing numbers.

(a)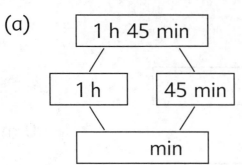

(b)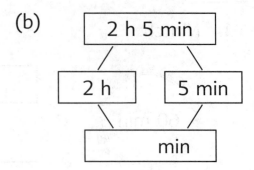

(c)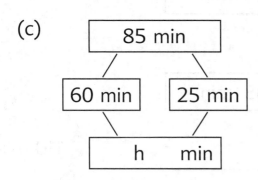

(d)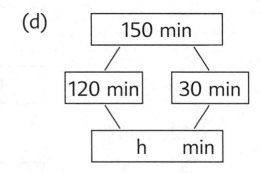

3. Write the following in minutes.

(a) 1 h 5 min = _____ min

(b) 1 h 30 min = _____ min

(c) 2 h 25 min = _____ min

(d) 3 h 10 min = _____ min

4. Write the following in hours and minutes.

(a) 75 min = _____ h _____ min

(b) 100 min = _____ h _____ min

(c) 140 min = _____ h _____ min

(d) 225 min = _____ h _____ min

EXERCISE 4

1. A film show started at 7:30 P.M.
   It lasted 1 h and 45 min.
   What time did the show end?

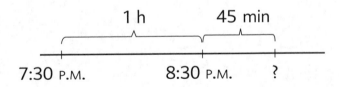

2. Amy started fishing at 4:40 P.M.
   She caught the first fish at 6:00 P.M.
   How long did she take to catch the first fish?

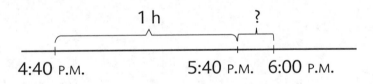

3. A concert started at 7:35 P.M.
   Cameron reached the theater 25 min before it started.
   What time did he reach the theater?

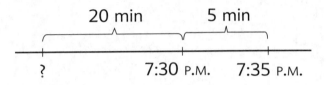

4. Hillary arrived at the airport at 7:40 P.M.
   The plane she was taking did not leave until 9:00 P.M.
   How long did she wait at the airport?

5. Travis drove from home to the zoo.
   He left home at 7:35 A.M. and arrived at the zoo
   45 min later.
   What time did he arrive at the zoo?

6. Jennifer took 1 h and 40 min to row her boat
   across the lake.
   Adam took 2 h and 5 min.
   How much longer did Adam take than Jennifer?

EXERCISE 5

1. Write the missing numbers.

   (a) 1 h 25 min + 30 min = _____ h _____ min

   25 min + 30 min = 55 min

   (b) 1 h 45 min + 40 min = _____ h _____ min

   (c) 2 h 30 min + 50 min = _____ h _____ min

   (d) 2 h 35 min + 35 min = _____ h _____ min

2. Write the missing numbers.

   (a) 1 h 50 min + 2 h 20 min = _____ h _____ min

   1 h 50 min $\xrightarrow{+2h}$ 3 h 50 min $\xrightarrow{+20min}$ 4 h 10 min

   (b) 1 h 45 min + 1 h 25 min = _____ h _____ min

   (c) 2 h 20 min + 1 h 50 min = _____ h _____ min

   (d) 2 h 40 min + 1 h 35 min = _____ h _____ min

   (e) 3 h 50 min + 1 h 20 min = _____ h _____ min

   (f) 3 h 25 min + 2 h 45 min = _____ h _____ min

3. Write the missing numbers.

(a) 1 h 45 min − 10 min = _____ h _____ min

45 min − 10 min = 35 min

(b) 2 h 40 min − 15 min = _____ h _____ min

(c) 2 h 5 min − 50 min = _____ h _____ min

(d) 3 h 35 min − 40 min = _____ h _____ min

4. Write the missing numbers.

(a) 2 h 30 min − 1 h 10 min = _____ h _____ min

2 h 30 min $\xrightarrow{-1\,h}$ 1 h 30 min $\xrightarrow{-10\,min}$ 1 h 20 min

(b) 3 h 45 min − 2 h 40 min = _____ h _____ min

(c) 2 h 50 min − 1 h 35 min = _____ h _____ min

(d) 3 h 15 min − 1 h 45 min = _____ h _____ min

(e) 4 h 5 min − 2 h 20 min = _____ h _____ min

(f) 4 h 20 min − 1 h 25 min = _____ h _____ min

EXERCISE 6

1. Work with your friends.
   You need a stopwatch.
   Measure the time taken for each
   of the following activities.

Activity	Time taken
Write the words SING A SONG.	_____ s
Walk 10 paces.	_____ s
Draw 5 triangles.	_____ s
Skip 15 times.	_____ s
Run 100 m.	_____ s

2. The table shows the time taken by 5 girls to swim 50 m.

Name	Time
Mary	59 s
Sara	55 s
Amy	57 s
Emily	54 s
Taylor	1 min

Study the table and fill in the blanks.

(a) _____ is the fastest swimmer.

(b) _____ is the slowest swimmer.

(c) Sara is faster than Mary by _____ seconds.

3. Write the missing numbers.

(a) 1 minute − 40 seconds = _____ seconds

(b) 1 minute − 34 seconds = _____ seconds

(c) 1 minute − 15 seconds = _____ seconds

(d) 1 minute − 26 seconds = _____ seconds

EXERCISE 7

1. Match.

1 min		65 s
1 min 5 s		60 s
1 min 45 s		105 s
2 min		145 s
2 min 25 s		215 s
3 min		120 s
3 min 35 s		180 s

2. Write the missing numbers.

(a)
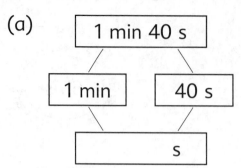

(b)
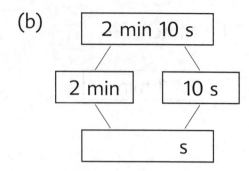

(c)
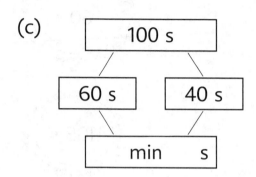

(d)
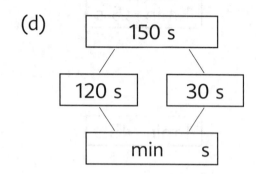

3. Write the following in seconds.

(a) 1 min 25 s = _____ s

(b) 2 min 45 s = _____ s

(c) 2 min 50 s = _____ s

(d) 3 min 30 s = _____ s

4. Write the following in minutes and seconds.

(a) 90 s = _____ min _____ s

(b) 115 s = _____ min _____ s

(c) 125 s = _____ min _____ s

(d) 200 s = _____ min _____ s

5. Fill in the blanks.

(a) 1 min 30 s = _____ s	(b) 1 min 55 s = _____ s
(c) 2 min 5 s = _____ s	(d) 2 min 30 s = _____ s
(e) 3 min 5 s = _____ s	(f) 3 min 40 s = _____ s
(g) 80 s = _____ min _____ s	(h) 85 s = _____ min _____ s
(i) 95 s = _____ min _____ s	(j) 110 s = _____ min _____ s
(k) 140 s = _____ min _____ s	(l) 165 s = _____ min _____ s

How many sides does a pentagon have?
Color the spaces that contain the answers to find out.

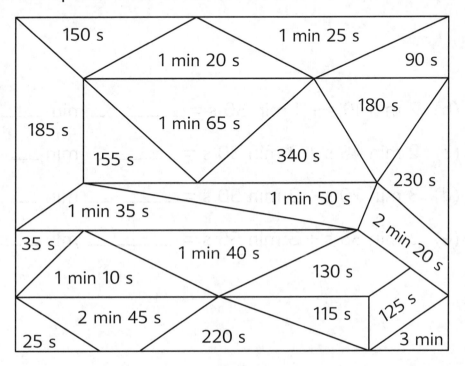

6. Add.

(a) 2 min 30 s + 15 s = _____ min _____ s

30 s + 15 s = 45 s

(b) 2 min 35 s + 20 s = _____ min _____ s

(c) 3 min 50 s + 30 s = _____ min _____ s

(d) 3 min 45 s + 45 s = _____ min _____ s

7. Add in compound units.

(a) 1 min 50 s + 3 min 40 s = _____ min _____ s

1 min 50 s $\xrightarrow{+\,3\,min}$ 4 min 50 s $\xrightarrow{+\,40\,s}$ 5 min 30 s

(b) 2 min 10 s + 1 min 50 s = _____ min _____ s

(c) 2 min 45 s + 2 min 30 s = _____ min _____ s

(d) 3 min 20 s + 2 min 50 s = _____ min _____ s

(e) 3 min 35 s + 3 min 55 s = _____ min _____ s

8. Subtract.

   (a) 2 min 50 s − 25 s = _____ min _____ s

   50 s − 25 s = 25 s

   (b) 2 min 45 s − 30 s = _____ min _____ s

   (c) 3 min 15 s − 25 s = _____ min _____ s

   (d) 3 min 20 s − 45 s = _____ min _____ s

9. Subtract in compound units.

   (a) 2 min 40 s − 1 min 25 s = _____ min _____ s

   2 min 40 s $\xrightarrow{-\ 1\ min}$ 1 min 40 s $\xrightarrow{-\ 25\ s}$ 1 min 15 s

   (b) 3 min 20 s − 1 min 50 s = _____ min _____ s

   (c) 3 min 35 s − 1 min 40 s = _____ min _____ s

   (d) 4 min 10 s − 2 min 25 s = _____ min _____ s

   (e) 5 min 5 s − 2 min 35 s = _____ min _____ s

EXERCISE 8

1. Match.

1 year 1 month	18 months
1 year 6 months	13 months
2 years	30 months
1 year 8 months	24 months
2 years 6 months	20 months
3 years	26 months
2 years 2 months	36 months

2. Write the missing numbers.

(a)
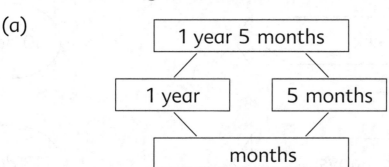

(b)
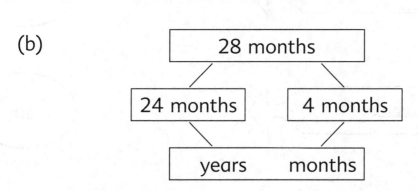

3. Write the following in months.

   (a) 1 year   3 months = _____ months

   (b) 2 years 5 months = _____ months

   (c) 2 years 11 months = _____ months

   (d) 3 years 10 months = _____ months

4. Write the following in years and months.

   (a) 15 months = _____ year _____ months

   (b) 26 months = _____ years _____ months

   (c) 32 months = _____ years _____ months

   (d) 40 months = _____ years _____ months

5. Match.

1 week	10 days
1 week 3 days	13 days
2 weeks	7 days
1 week 6 days	20 days
2 weeks 2 days	14 days
2 weeks 6 days	16 days
3 weeks 1 day	22 days

6. Write the missing numbers.

(a)

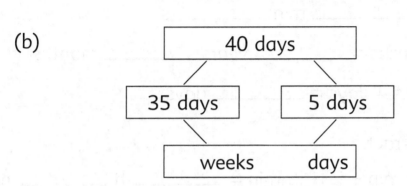

(b)

7. Write the following in days.

(a) 1 week   5 days = _____ days

(b) 2 weeks 4 days = _____ days

(c) 3 weeks 3 days = _____ days

(d) 4 weeks 2 days = _____ days

8. Write the following in weeks and days.

(a) 12 days = _____ week _____ days

(b) 25 days = _____ weeks _____ days

(c) 30 days = _____ weeks _____ days

(d) 32 days = _____ weeks _____ days

REVIEW 10

1. Find the missing numbers.

   (a) 3 h 25 min = _____ min

   (b) 132 min = _____ h _____ min

   (c) 2 min 20 s = _____ s

   (d) 83 s = _____ min _____ s

   (e) 27 months = _____ years _____ months

   (f) 3 weeks 4 days = _____ days

2. Add or subtract.

   (a) 2 h 30 min + 2 h 15 min = _____ h _____ min

   (b) 4 min 35 s − 2 min 20 s = _____ min _____ s

   (c) 1 h 50 min + 1 h 50 min = _____ h _____ min

   (d) 3 h 5 min − 1 h 45 min = _____ h _____ min

   (e) 3 min 40 s + 2 min 55 s = _____ min _____ s

   (f) 3 min 15 s − 1 min 45 s = _____ min _____ s

3. Fill in the blanks.

   (a) At a zoo, the tigers are fed at 9:45 A.M.
        The lions are fed 40 minutes later.

        The lions are fed at _____.

   (b) A concert started at 1:20 P.M.
        Alice and her friends arrived at the theater
        at 12:50 P.M.

        They were _____ minutes early.

4. Anson left home at 8:45 A.M.
    He took the subway and reached his office at 9:30 A.M.
    How long did he take to get to work from home?

_____

5. Mrs. Mary took a photography class that began at 8:30 A.M.
    The class was 7 h 30 min long.
    What time did the photography class end?

_____

6. A bus ride from San Francisco to Los Angeles takes
    6 h 45 min.
    A bus ride from Los Angeles to San Diego takes 3 h 55 min.
    If there is no break between the bus transfers, how long
    does it take to get to San Diego from San Francisco?

EXERCISE 1

1. A group of children made this picture graph to show the times at which they get up in the morning.

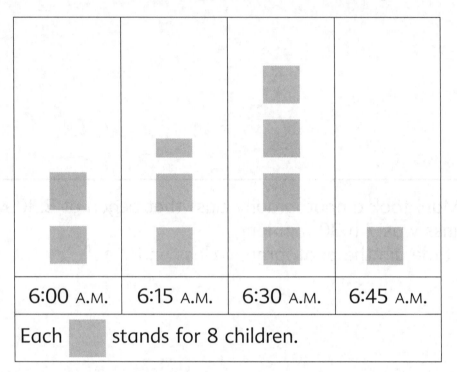

Study the graph and fill in the blanks.

(a) _____ children get up at 6:15 A.M.

(b) _____ more children get up at 6:00 A.M. than at 6:45 A.M.

(c) The greatest number of children get up at _____.

(d) _____ children get up before 6:30 A.M.

2. This table represents the number of books read by four children in one year.

Name	Number of books
David	80
Ricki	165
Lauren	140
Rosa	95

(a) Who read the greatest number of books in one year?

  _____

(b) How many more books did Lauren read than David in one year? _____

(c) Decide on a suitable scale and symbol for this data and complete the picture graph.

David	Ricki	Lauren	Rosa

Each _____ stands for _____ books.

3. Here are the savings of five children.

Complete the following graph to show the given data.

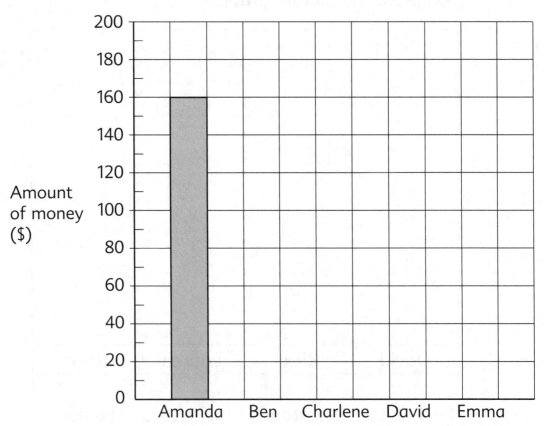

4. This tally chart shows the number of DVDs sold in four shops in a week.

Shop	Number of DVDs sold
A	~~IIII~~ ~~IIII~~ ~~IIII~~ ~~IIII~~
B	~~IIII~~ ~~IIII~~ ~~IIII~~ ~~IIII~~ ~~IIII~~ ~~IIII~~ ~~IIII~~ ~~IIII~~ ~~IIII~~
C	~~IIII~~ ~~IIII~~ ~~IIII~~ ~~IIII~~ ~~IIII~~ ~~IIII~~
D	~~IIII~~ ~~IIII~~ ~~IIII~~ ~~IIII~~ ~~IIII~~ ~~IIII~~ ~~IIII~~ ~~IIII~~

Complete the following graph to show the data given in the table.

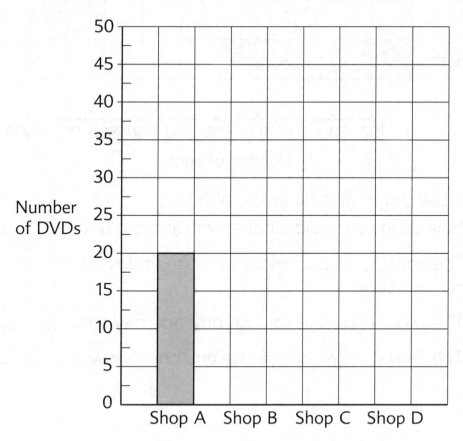

5. This bar graph shows the number of eggs Lindsey sold from Monday to Friday.

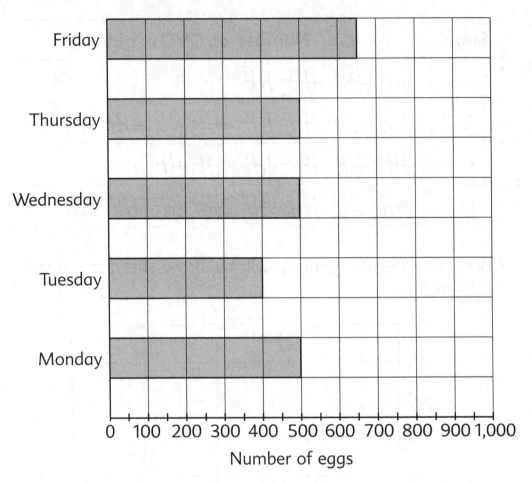

Number of eggs

Study the graph and fill in the blanks.

(a) How many eggs did Lindsey sell on most days? _____

(b) She sold _____ more eggs on Friday than on Thursday.

(c) The most eggs she sold on any one day was _____ .

(d) The fewest eggs she sold on any one day was _____ .

6. The bar graph shows the number of T-shirts sold by Mr. Cohen from Monday to Friday.

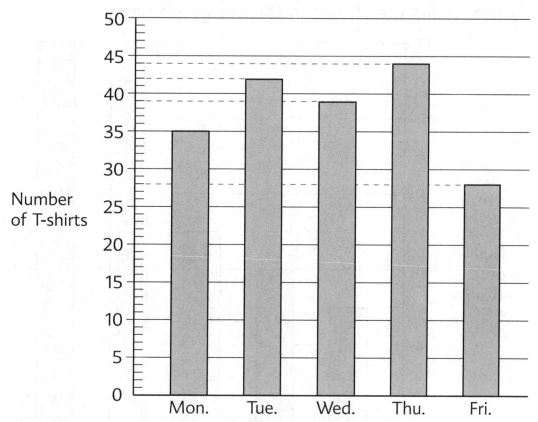

Number of T-shirts

Study the graph and answer the questions.

(a) On which day did Mr. Cohen sell the greatest number of T-shirts? _____

(b) How many T-shirts did he sell on Wednesday? _____

(c) On which day did he sell 28 T-shirts? _____

(d) How many more T-shirts did he sell on Tuesday than on Monday? _____

(e) If the T-shirts were sold at $8 each, how much did Mr. Cohen collect from the sale of the T-shirts? _____

7. A group of children were asked to choose which type of story they liked best.
The results are shown in the bar graph below.

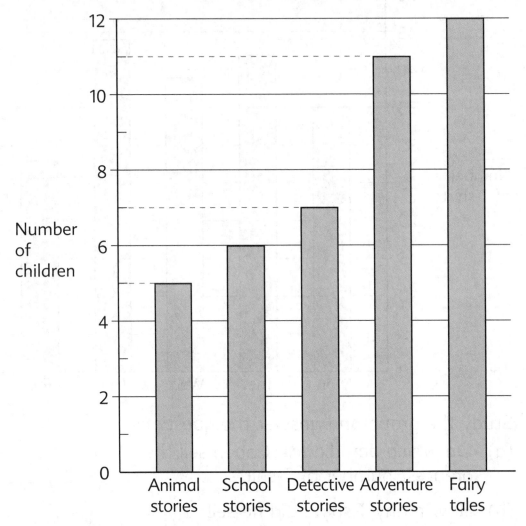

Study the graph and answer the questions.

(a) Which type of stories was the most popular? _____

(b) How many children liked animal stories? _____

(c) Which type of stories was twice as popular as school stories? _____

(d) How many more children liked adventure stories than detective stories? _____

(e) If there were 15 boys in the group, how many girls were there? _____

EXERCISE 2

1. Measure each of these lines to the nearest fourth of an inch.
    Then complete the line plot.

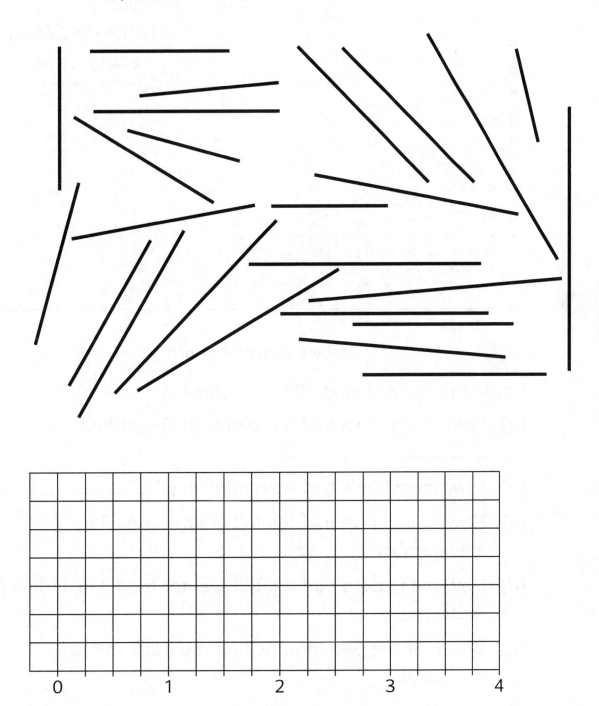

2. Alexa measured the rainfall in her backyard to the nearest eighth of an inch in December and in June.
She created the following line plot.

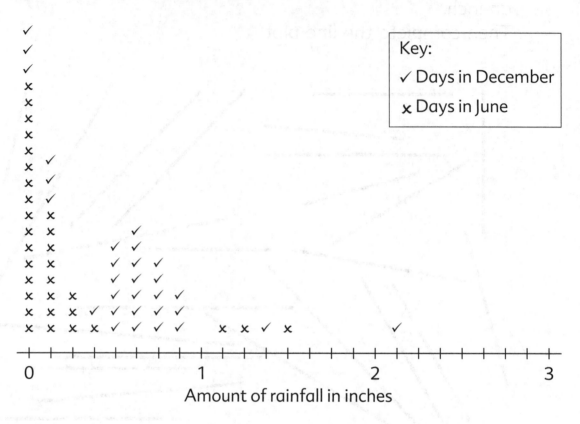

Study the line plot and fill in the blanks.

(a) How many days had no rainfall in December?

_____

(b) How many days had no rainfall in June? _____

(c) How many days had rainfall greater than 1 in. in December? _____

(d) How many days had rainfall greater than 1 in. in June?

_____

(e) Which of the two months had the most rainfall?

_____

REVIEW 11

1. The table shows the points scored by four students on a test.

Name	Points
David	80
Betty	60
Andy	75
Cathy	95

(a) Who scored 20 points more than Betty? _____

(b) Who scored 20 points less than Cathy? _____

(c) Select a suitable scale and create a picture graph for this data.

David	Andy	Betty	Cathy

Each _____ stands for _____ points.

2. The graph below shows the number of third grade students going to school by bus.

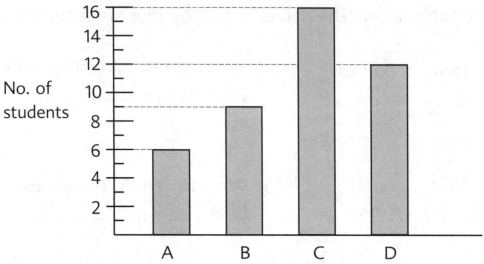

(a) Find the total number of students coming to school by bus. _____

(b) Which class has the most number of students coming to school by bus? _____

3. The graph below shows Larry's savings for 6 months.

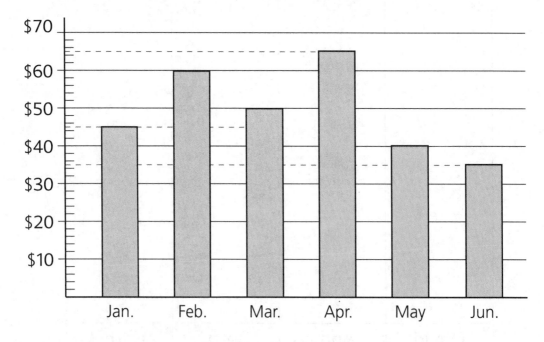

(a) Find his total savings for the 6 months. _____

(b) In which month did Larry save the least money? _____

4. The table shows the number of third grade students wearing glasses.

Class	No. of students wearing glasses
3A	6
3B	14
3C	10
3D	4

(a) How many students wear glasses? _____

(b) Use the data given in the table to complete the bar graph below.

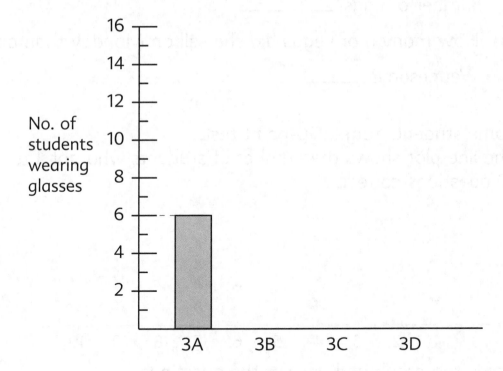

5. The graph shows the number of eggs Wendy sold in 5 days.

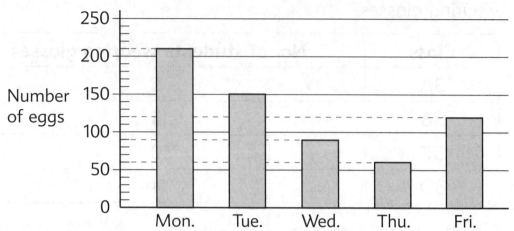

Study the graph and answer the questions.

(a) On which day did Wendy sell the least

   number of eggs? _____

(b) How many more eggs did she sell on Monday than on

   Wednesday? _____

6. Some students took a 10-point test.
The line plot shows the number of students who got 1 to
10 questions correct.

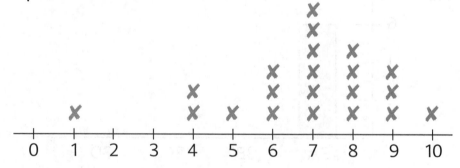

Study the graph and answer the questions.

(a) How many children took the test? _____

(b) What score did most children get? _____

(c) How many children got a score greater than 6? _____

(d) How many children got a score less than 5? _____

(e) What fraction of the children got a score
   less than 5? _____

EXERCISE 1

1. Check (✓) the correct answer for each angle.

Angle	Smaller than a right angle	Bigger than a right angle	Equal to a right angle
a			
b			
c			
d			
e			

2. Each of the following triangles has a right angle.
   Mark the right angle.

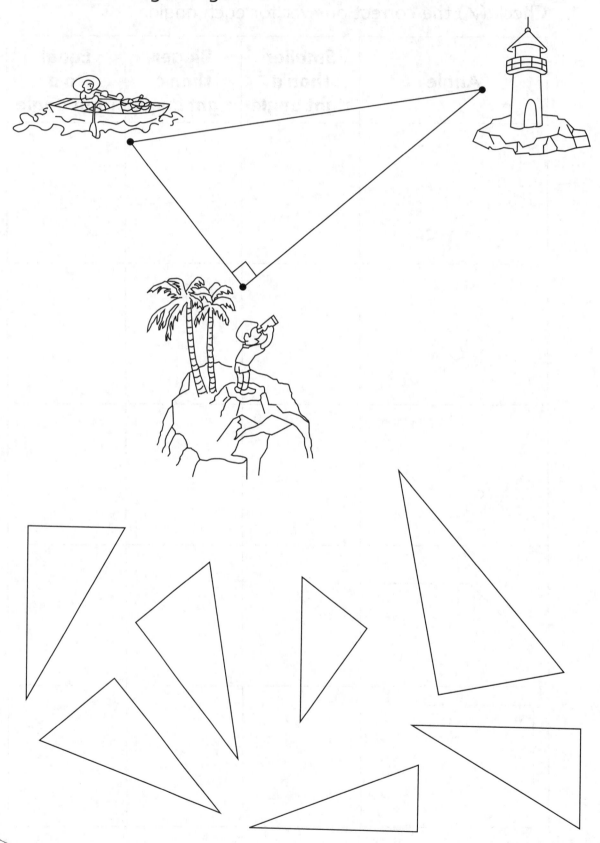

EXERCISE 2

1. Complete the table below.

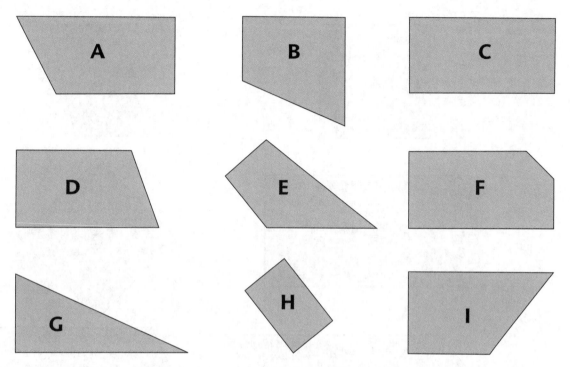

Figure	Number of sides	Number of angles	Number of right angles
A			
B			
C			
D			
E			
F			
G			
H			
I			

2. Write the letter for each shape in the correct column below.
   The same shape may go in more than one column.

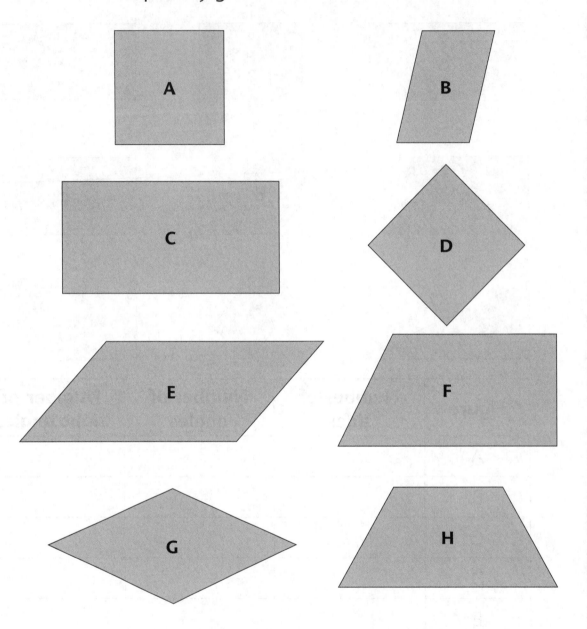

Quadrilateral	Rhombus	Rectangle	Square

3. Use the corner of a card to help you draw a right angle.

   (a) Draw a quadrilateral with only one right angle.

   (b) Draw a quadrilateral with only two right angles.

   (c) Draw a quadrilateral with no right angles.

REVIEW 12

1. How many sides and angles does each figure have?

(a)

_____ sides

_____ angles

(b)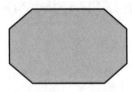

_____ sides

_____ angles

2. Which angle is a right angle?

Angle _____ is a right angle.

3.

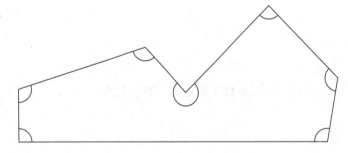

(a) How many of the marked angles are right angles?

_____

(b) How many of the marked angles are smaller than a right angle? _____

(c) How many of the marked angles are greater than a right angle? _____

4. Write the letter for each shape in the correct column below.
   The same shape may go into more than one column.
   Some shapes may not belong to any of the columns.

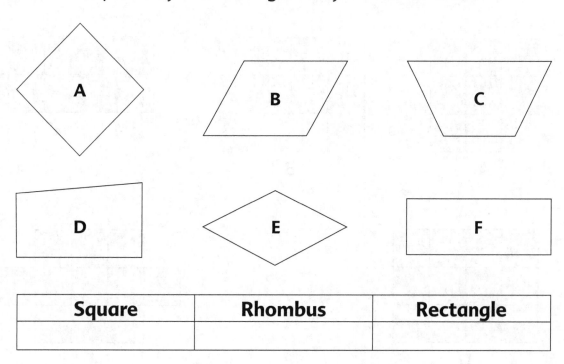

Square	Rhombus	Rectangle

5. (a) Draw a quadrilateral with four right angles. What is the
       shape of this figure?

   (b) Draw another quadrilateral with four right angles and
       four equal sides. What is the shape of this figure?

EXERCISE 1

1. What is the area of each of the following figures?

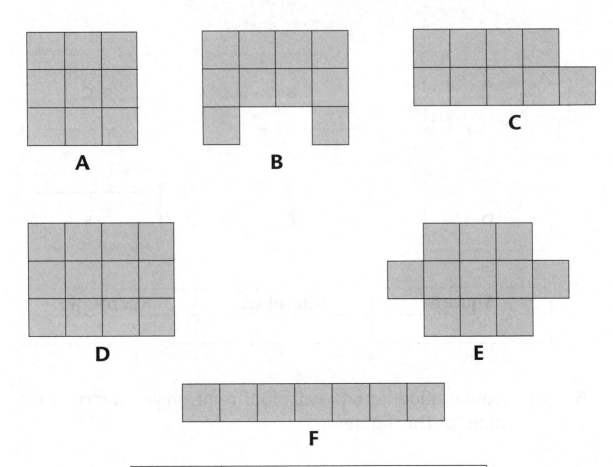

Figure	Area
A	square units
B	square units
C	square units
D	square units
E	square units
F	square units

2. What is the area of each of the following figures?

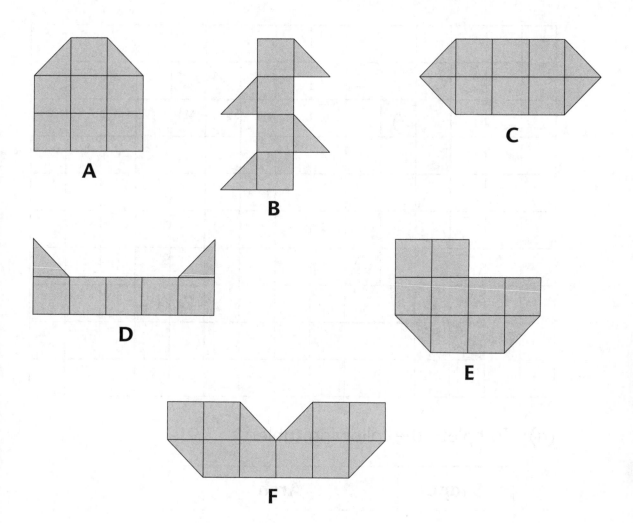

Figure	Area
A	square units
B	square units
C	square units
D	square units
E	square units
F	square units

3. Study the figures and answer the following.

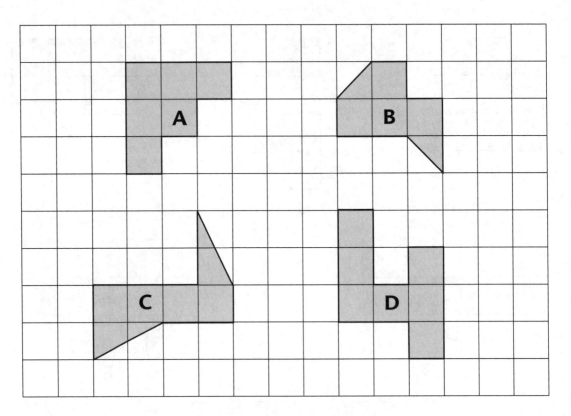

(a) Complete the following table.

Shape	Area
A	square units
B	square units
C	square units
D	square units

(b) Shape _____ has the greatest area.

(c) Shape _____ has the smallest area.

(d) Shape _____ and Shape _____ have the same area.

4. Circle the shape with the greater area in each pair.

(a)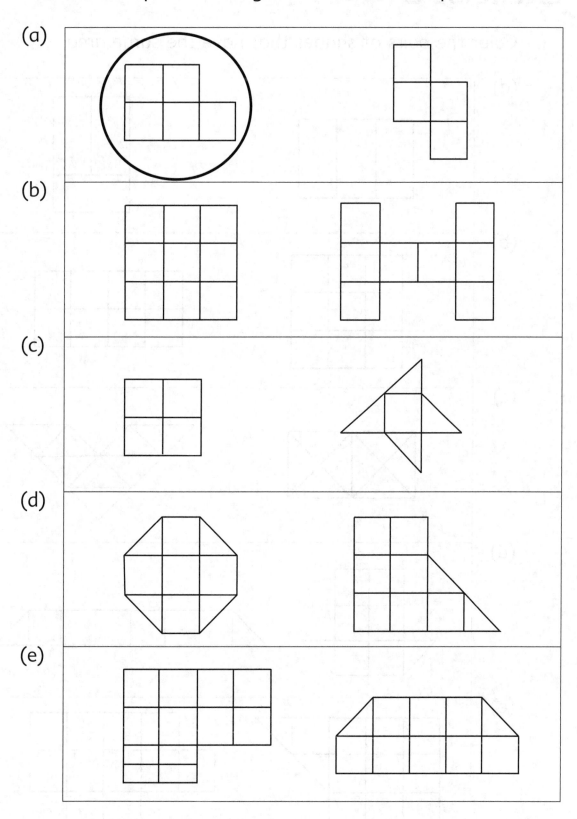

(b)

(c)

(d)

(e)

EXERCISE 2

1. Color the pairs of shapes that have the same area.

(a)

(b)

(c)

(d)

(e)

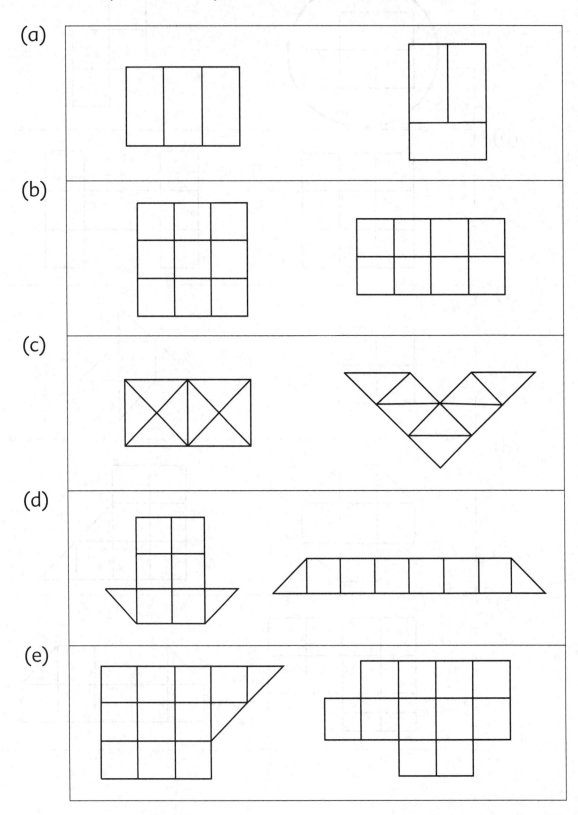

2. Match the two shapes that have the same area.

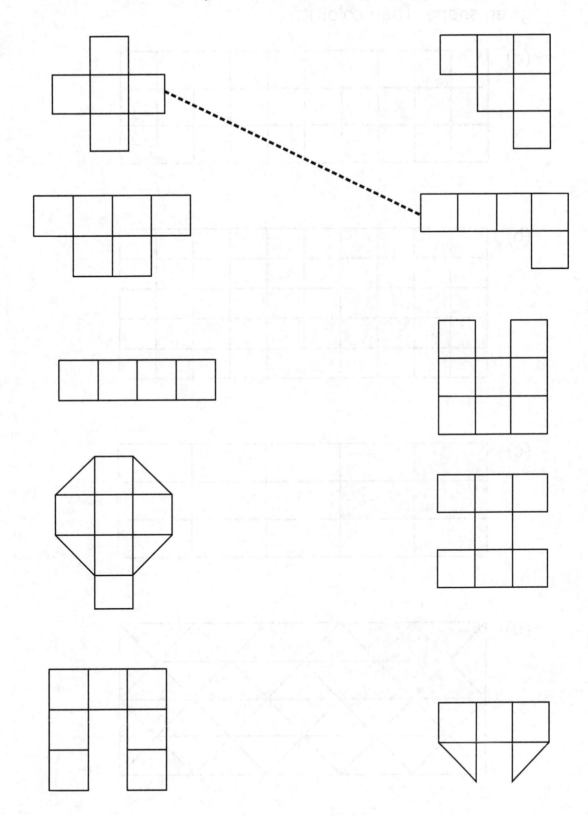

3. Draw another shape that has the same area as the given shape. Then color it.

(a)

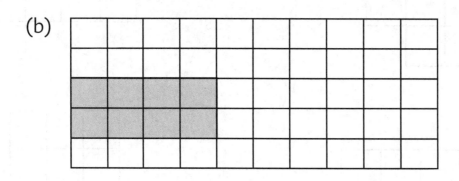

(b)

(c)

(d)

4. What is the area of each shape?

(a)

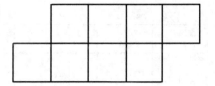

The area is _____ square units.

(b)

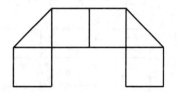

The area is _____ square units.

(c)

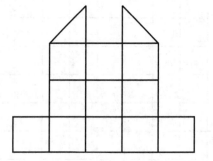

The area is _____ square units.

(d)

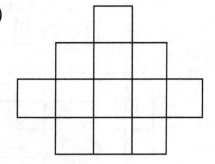

The area is _____ square units.

(e)

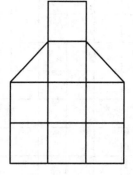

The area is _____ square units.

(f)

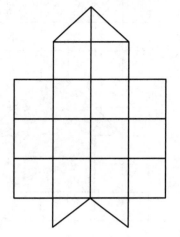

The area is _____ square units.

5. Draw another shape that has the same area as the given shape. Then color it.

(a)

(b)

(c)

(d)

(e)

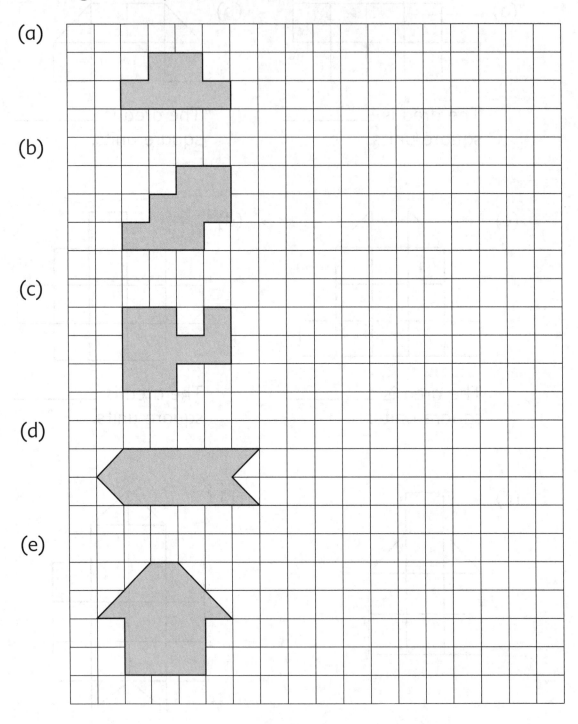

EXERCISE 3

1. What is the area of each of the following figures?

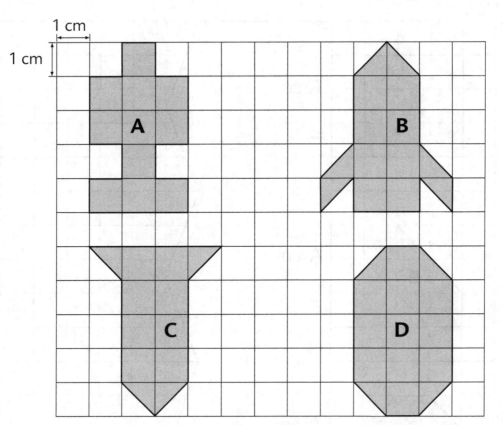

Figure	Area
A	square centimeters
B	square centimeters
C	square centimeters
D	square centimeters

Figure _____ and Figure _____ have the same area.

Figure _____ has the biggest area.

Figure _____ has the smallest area.

2. Write the area of each of the following figures.
   Then draw another figure of the same area.

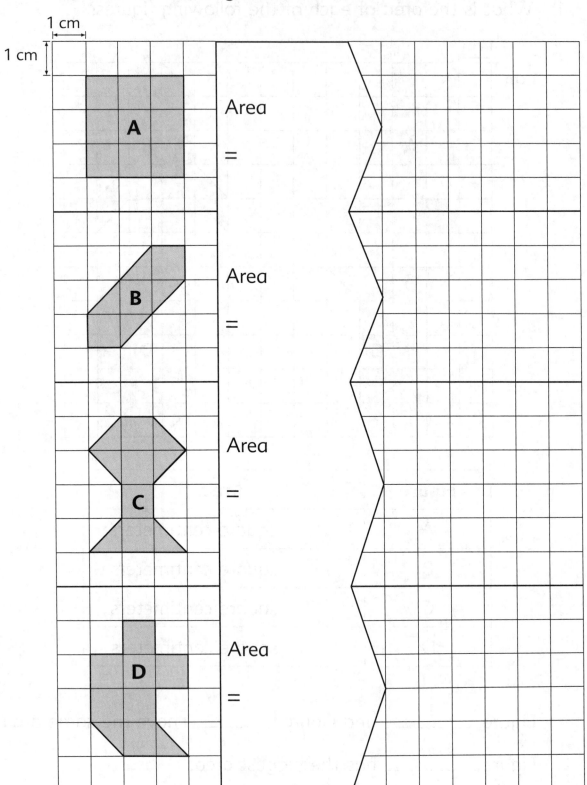

1 cm

1 cm

Area

=

Area

=

Area

=

Area

=

3. What is the area of each of the following figures?

(a)

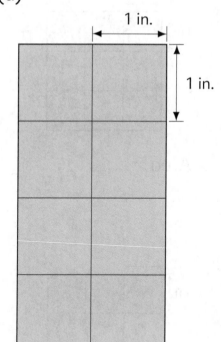

Area =

(b)

1 in.

1 in.

Area =

(c)

1 in.

1 in.

Area =

(d)

1 in.

1 in.

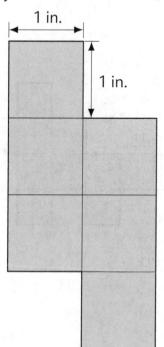

Area =

4. What is the area of each of the following figures?

(a)

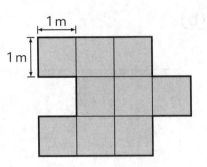

Area =

(b)

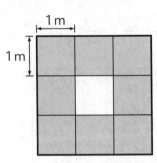

Area =

(c)

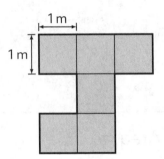

Area =

(d)

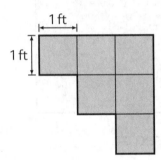

Area =

(e)

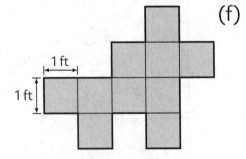

Area =

(f)

Area =

EXERCISE 4

1. Measure the perimeter in centimeters of each of the following figures.

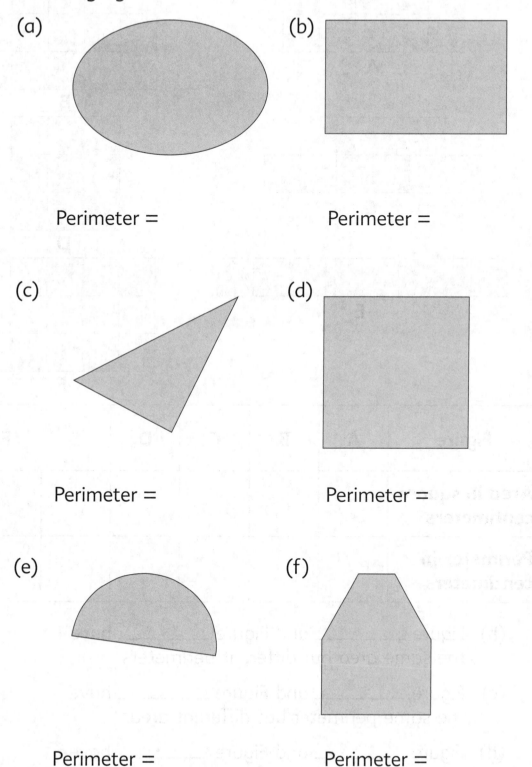

(a)

Perimeter =

(b)

Perimeter =

(c)

Perimeter =

(d)

Perimeter =

(e)

Perimeter =

(f)

Perimeter =

2. The following figures are made up of 1-cm squares.
   (a) Find the area and the perimeter of each figure.

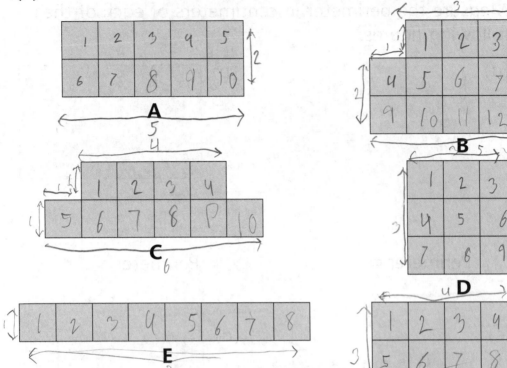

Figure	A	B	C	D	E	F
Area in square centimeters	10	13	10	9	8	13
Perimeter in centimeters	14	12	16	12	16	16

(b) Figure _____ and Figure _____ have the same area but different perimeters.

(c) Figure _____ and Figure _____ have the same perimeter but different areas.

(d) Figure _____ and Figure _____ have the same area and perimeter.

EXERCISE 5

1. Find the perimeter of each of the following figures:

(a)

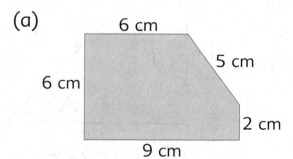

6 cm
5 cm
6 cm
2 cm
9 cm

Perimeter =

(b)

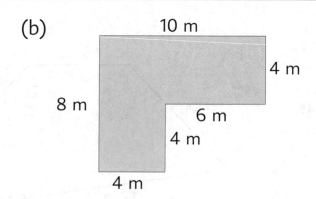

10 m
4 m
8 m
6 m
4 m
4 m

Perimeter =

(c)

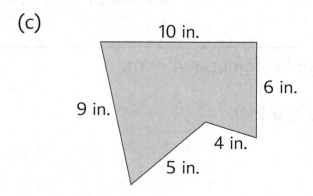

10 in.
6 in.
9 in.
4 in.
5 in.

Perimeter =

(d)

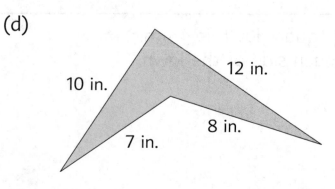

12 in.
10 in.
8 in.
7 in.

Perimeter =

2. Find the missing side length of each of the following figures:

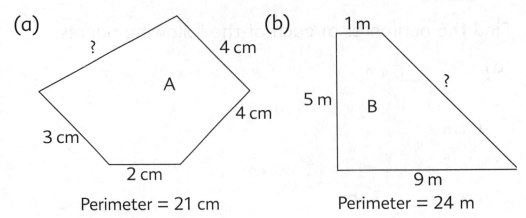

(a)
?
4 cm
A
4 cm
3 cm
2 cm
Perimeter = 21 cm

(b)
1 m
5 m
B
?
9 m
Perimeter = 24 m

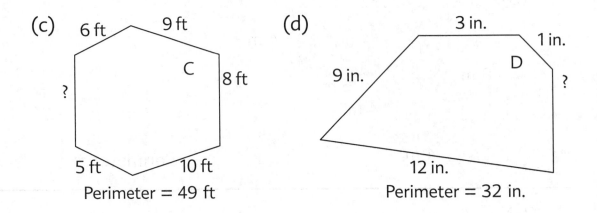

(c)
6 ft   9 ft
C
8 ft
?
5 ft   10 ft
Perimeter = 49 ft

(d)
3 in.
1 in.
D
9 in.
?
12 in.
Perimeter = 32 in.

---

3. The length of a rectangular folder is 45 cm.
    Its width is 30 cm.
    Find the perimeter of the folder.

---

4. The perimeter of a square lawn is 48 m.
    Find the length of each side of the lawn.

EXERCISE 6

1. Write down the length and width of each rectangle.
   Then multiply the length and width to find the area of
   the rectangle.

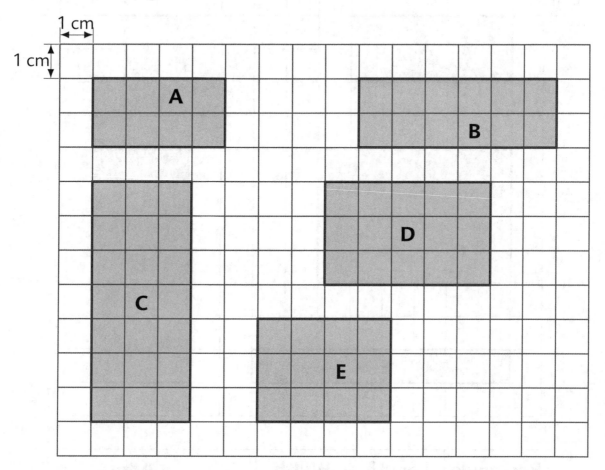

Rectangle	Length	Width	Area
A	4 cm	2 cm	8 square centimeters
B			
C			
D			
E			

2. Find the area of each rectangle by multiplying its length and width.

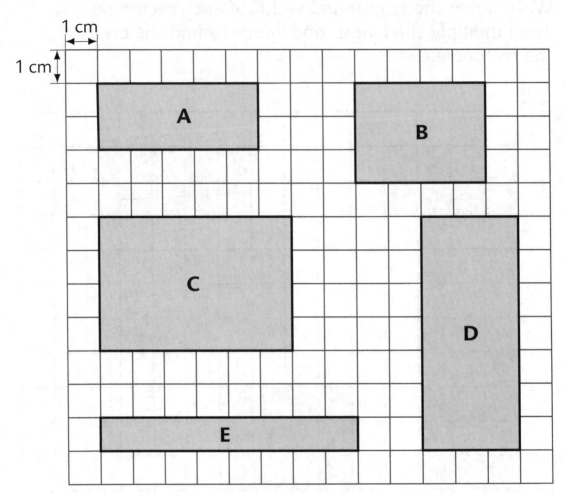

Rectangle	Length	Width	Area
A	5 cm	2 cm	10 square centimeters
B			
C			
D			
E			

3. Find the area of each rectangle.

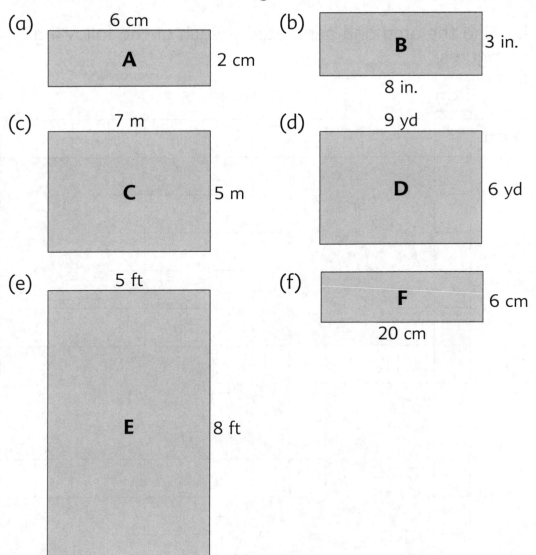

(a) 6 cm
A
2 cm

(b) B
3 in.
8 in.

(c) 7 m
C
5 m

(d) 9 yd
D
6 yd

(e) 5 ft
E
8 ft

(f) F
6 cm
20 cm

Rectangle	Area
A	12 square centimeters
B	
C	
D	
E	
F	

EXERCISE 7

1. Find the area and perimeter of each of the following figures.

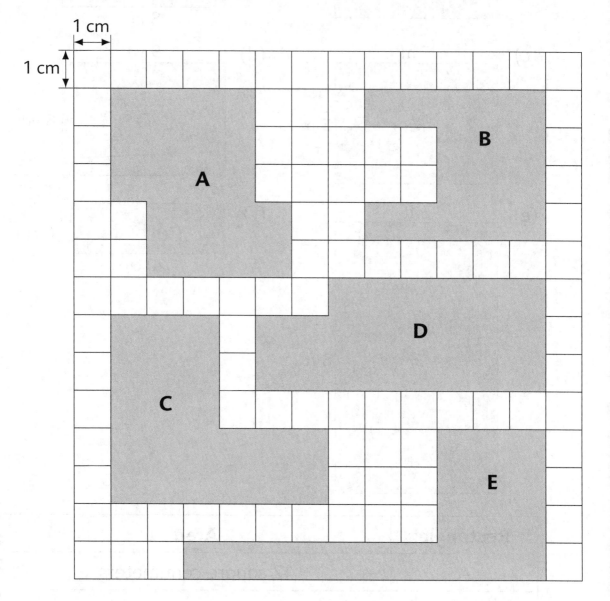

A.   Area = _____   Perimeter = _____

B.   Area = _____   Perimeter = _____

C.   Area = _____   Perimeter = _____

D.   Area = _____   Perimeter = _____

E.   Area = _____   Perimeter = _____

2. The figure below is made up of two rectangles and a square.
   Find the area and the perimeter.

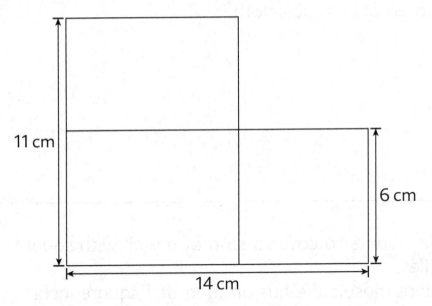

11 cm

6 cm

14 cm

Area = _____ Perimeter = _____

3. The entrance and living room of a house need to be carpeted.
   The living room has an L shape consisting of two squares.
   The entrance is also shaped like a square.
   The carpet and padding cost $8 per square yard.
   How much will it cost to carpet the two rooms? _____

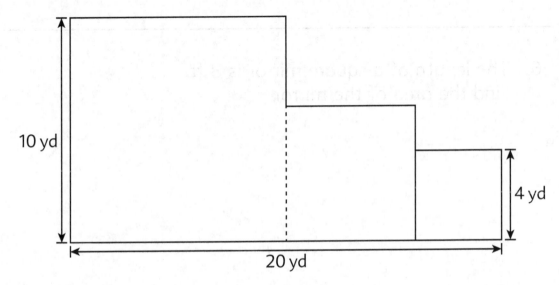

10 yd

4 yd

20 yd

4. The length of a tablecloth is 4 m.
   Its width is 2 m.
   Find the area of the tablecloth.

---

5. Mrs. Wiley wants to cover a strip of a wall with square mosaic tiles.
   Each square mosaic tile has an area of 1 square inch.
   The strip of wall has a length of 90 in. and a width of 9 in.
   How many square mosaic tiles must she use to cover the strip of wall?

---

6. The length of a square mirror is 8 ft.
   Find the area of the mirror.

REVIEW 13

1. Find the area and perimeter of each figure.

   (a)

   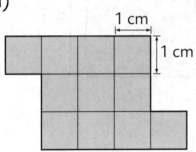

   (b)

   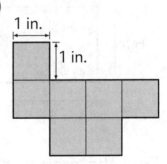

   Area = _____   Area = _____

   Perimeter = _____   Perimeter = _____

2. Find the perimeter of each figure.

   (a)

   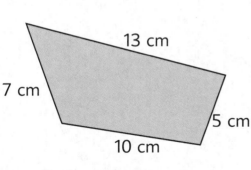

   13 cm

   7 cm

   5 cm

   10 cm

   (b)

   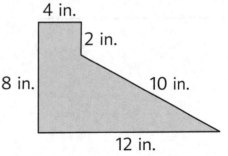

   4 in.

   2 in.

   8 in.

   10 in.

   12 in.

   Perimeter = _____   Perimeter = _____

3. The rectangle and the square have the same perimeter. Find their areas.

   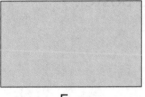

   3 cm

   5 cm

   (a) The area of the rectangle is _____.

   (b) The area of the square is _____.

4. The following figure is made up of a rectangle and a square.

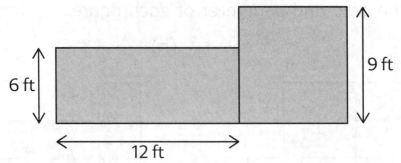

(a) Find the area of the figure. _____

(b) Find the perimeter of the figure. _____

5. Mrs. Todd mowed a rectangular lawn with a length of 7 m and a width of 6 m.
   What was the area of the lawn that she mowed?

   _____

6. Ryan placed a square poster in a café.
   The perimeter of the poster was 116 cm.
   Find the length of each side of the poster.

   _____

7. A rectangular field measures 40 m by 30 m.
What is the cost of putting up a fence around it if 1 m of fencing costs $7?

---

8. Jane uses 30 old stamps to make a picture.
If each stamp measures 3 cm by 2 cm, find the area of the picture.

---

9. It costs $9 a square yard to carpet the floor of a room.
If the floor of the room is 5 yd long and 4 yd wide, find the cost of carpeting the floor of the room.

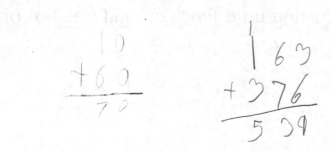

$$\begin{array}{r} 10 \\ +60 \\ \hline 70 \end{array}$$

$$\begin{array}{r} 163 \\ +376 \\ \hline 539 \end{array}$$

$$\begin{array}{r} 79 \\ -68 \\ \hline 11 \end{array}$$

$$\begin{array}{r} {}^{6}\cancel{7}\,{}^{16}\cancel{6} \\ -48 \\ \hline 28 \end{array}$$

BLANK